*Rocks and Minerals*

## About the Author

Richard M. Pearl, a graduate of the University of Colorado and Harvard University, is now Professor of Geology at Colorado College. He is a fellow of the American Association for the Advancement of Science, the Gemmological Association of Great. Britain, and the Meteoritical Society, and has received honorary titles from national gem societies in a number of countries. He has been president of the American Federation of Mineralogical Societies, the Rocky Mountain Federation of Mineral Societies, and the Colorado Mineral Society. Professor Pearl is the author of seventeen books on geology, minerals, and gems, including *Guide to Geologic Literature, Popular Gemology, How to Know the Minerals and Rocks, 1001 Questions Answered About the Mineral Kingdom.*

# Rocks and Minerals

Revised Edition

Richard M. Pearl

BARNES & NOBLE, INC. NEW YORK

Publishers • Booksellers • Since 1873

*an Everyday Handbook*

This is an original Everyday Handbook (Number 260). It was written by a distinguished educator, carefully edited, and manufactured in the United States of America in keeping with the highest standards of publishing.

# Preface

*Rocks and Minerals* is intended to present in popular language for the general reader the most recent accurate knowledge about the entire range of the mineral kingdom, a subject of ever-growing significance in this second half of the twentieth century. It covers minerals and rocks, ores and metals, gems, crystals, and meteorites, as well as artificial minerals—from their origin and world-wide occurrence to their current industrial uses.

This book explains how rocks and minerals are classified, how they can be recognized and identified, and how they should be collected and displayed. Radioactive minerals are emphasized, befitting their strategic importance in today's peacetime economy and international tension. Fluorescent minerals, another area of outstanding interest, are also given special treatment, as are meteorites, which are yet the only tangible evidence of the outer space into which man is just beginning to venture. Prospecting for uranium and other minerals is described, together with the methods of mining them.

Italics emphasize essential scientific terms when they are first presented in the text. A selected, annotated reading list is given, along with a list of the national magazines in the United States devoted to the mineral-collecting hobby. A glossary and a classified index are other features of this book. The photographs and drawings are well chosen to illustrate the text.

In this edition, Chapter 12 has been revised, the Bibliography has been expanded, and minor changes appear elsewhere.

R. M. P.

# Acknowledgments

Thanks are due for information given by Robert A. Hatch, Mineralogist, United States Bureau of Mines, Norris, Tennessee, and W. D. George, Chief, High Frequency Standards Branch, United States Bureau of Standards, Boulder, Colorado.

The colored photographs have been obtained through the courtesy of Thomas S. Warren, President, Ultra-Violet Products, Inc., South Pasadena, California, and David E. Jensen, Head of the Geological Department, Ward's Natural Science Establishment, Rochester, N.Y.

The black and white photographs are credited in the preferred places, but I wish to express gratitude to the following individuals for their generous assistance: Hon. Thor Thors, Minister of Iceland to the United States; Henry L. Gresham and David E. Jensen, Head of the Geological Department, Ward's Natural Science Establishment, Rochester, N.Y.; Dr. Harvey H. Nininger, Director, American Meteorite Museum, Sedona, Ariz.; Florence Le Dosquet and George D. Skinner, N. W. Ayer and Son, Inc., New York; H. C. Meyer, Chairman of the Board, Foote Mineral Company, Philadelphia; Cleveland Lane, Manager of Public Relations, Pennsylvania Salt Manufacturing Company, Philadelphia; Eldridge Miller, Johns-Manville Sales Corporation, New York; Carl H. Pihl, Assistant to Secretary, Copper and Brass Research Association, New York.

The sketches of atomic structure were drawn by my student Henry Paddon.

The author wishes to express his sincere gratitude to Dr. Samuel Smith and Mrs. Marcia Dansky Amstell, of the Barnes and Noble editorial department, for their generous contributions to this book.

*To my father*

# Table of Contents

*Rocks and Minerals*

# Our World of Minerals

Truly we live in a world of minerals! Our bodies are nourished by minerals, and our activities and material progress on this planet Earth are influenced greatly by the distribution and availability of minerals.

The soil which supports all forms of life on land—vegetation (flora) directly, and animals (fauna) indirectly—consists of broken and decomposed minerals and rocks, with added products of decaying organic matter from previous generations of plants. Thus are the animal, vegetable, and mineral kingdoms interdependent, the mineral kingdom being the primary division in the cycle of events. Minerals enable plants to grow, and animals, including man, flourish in this favorable environment. Marine life, which is far more abundant than life on land, feeds upon the mineral salts that have been dissolved from the continents during the long history of our globe.

Water, the most essential of all food materials, is an exceedingly vital part of the mineral kingdom. This kingdom also comprises the streams, lakes, and other water bodies ranging in size up to the vast oceans, as well as the subsurface fluid—the "waters under the earth"—and the rain and snow that contribute generously to them all.

The term mineral, however, is often employed in a practical way, which is broader than this restricted usage so dear to the precise mind of the mineralogist. In England, for instance, a dealer in "minerals" actually sells, for whatever its medicinal value, water from mineralized springs. A land deed that specifies "mineral rights" includes petroleum and other substances of the mineral kingdom that are not true minerals. Even the geologist speaks of mineral resources in this wider sense and includes underground water, oil and natural gas, and numerous rock products. In popular language, artificial metals such as steel are referred to as minerals.

## CHARACTERISTICS OF MINERALS

Scientifically, a mineral is defined as a homogeneous substance which has a specific chemical composition and is produced by natural inorganic processes. Most minerals also have a definite internal structure which often is expressed in typical outward forms called crystals.

Being homogeneous, a mineral is shown to consist of a single uniform area when viewed under a microscope. This is unlike the majority of rocks, which are revealed upon magnification to be aggregates of several different minerals, or a combination of minerals and natural glass, even though they may appear to the unaided eye to be the same substance throughout.

The composition of a mineral, furthermore, must be capable of being represented by chemical symbols in a chemical formula, which either is rigidly fixed or else is variable according to a dependable law. Diamond, for example, is practically pure carbon and its formula can be expressed by the letter $C$, which is the abbreviation of the word carbon and stands as the symbol for this element. At the other extreme is a mineral such as hornblende, with the general formula $Ca_2Na\,(Mg,Fe)_4\,(Al,Fe,Ti)\,(Al,Si)_8O_{22}\,(O,OH)_2$. This chemical shorthand states with reasonable exactness the kind and number of elements that constitute this important mineral and the way in which they are combined in it, as further explained on page 52.

Artificial materials, such as synthetic gems and manufactured chemicals, are excluded from the ranks of minerals because they are not entirely of natural origin.

Products of animal or vegetable life likewise cannot be regarded as minerals because they have had an organic instead of an inorganic source.

These specifications, therefore, limit the true minerals to perhaps 1,500 different species, the accepted number depending upon how they are classified (see Chapter 4). The definite internal structure usually associated with minerals implies the existence of a three-dimensional pattern of atoms, the arrangement of which is intimately related to the crystal form and to other essential properties. Only a very few minerals, such as opal, do not have this regularity of atomic spacing.

## ROCKS, GEMS, AND STONES

Rocks—the other branch of the mineral kingdom—include the earth substances that fail to satisfy the fairly strict requirements demanded of a mineral. The significance of a rock as an adequate sample of a given part of the earth has already been mentioned. Most rocks are aggregates of two or more materials, whether minerals or glass. Granite is representative of this kind of rock; it is composed of the minerals quartz and feldspar, usually with smaller amounts of other minerals, especially mica and hornblende. Basalt, a common volcanic rock, sometimes appears quite homogeneous until a piece of it is ground thin enough to be transparent to light, and then a microscope reveals that it consists of tiny grains of several minerals, often with particles of natural glass interspersed among them. Hence the typical rock is a mixture or aggregate of a number of different substances, which may be either minerals or glass.

A second kind of rock consists of just a single mineral, but one which is abundant enough in a given area so that it may be regarded as a prominent part of the structure of the earth. The mineral halite, or common salt, becomes such a rock when it exists in extensive beds or layers, some of which may underlie large areas and be hundreds of feet thick. The immense salt deposits of New York, Pennsylvania, and Ohio are believed to be connected with those of Michigan and Ontario beneath the waters of the Great Lakes. They were formed in a distant time when this eastern part of the Great Lakes region, now famed for its fruit orchards, was a huge inland dead sea slowly drying to a desert. Sandstone is another rock made up of grains of one mineral, quartz; though other minerals may also be present, some sandstones, such as the St. Peter sandstone of Minnesota and adjacent states, are remarkably pure.

A third type of rock is likewise homogeneous and could almost be considered a mineral, except that the chemical composition varies irregularly. Ordinary black obsidian, for example, is a volcanic glass, uniform in appearance and seemingly much the same no matter where it occurs. Yet, the chemist finds the proportions of its constituents to vary from place to place, so that no standard chemical formula can be written for it. Such a substance is a rock instead of a mineral, but if it had crystallized from its glassy state, obsidian would have become an aggregate of several minerals—in fact, a typical granite.

The fourth kind of rock is of organic origin. Coal, which belongs in this category, is derived from plants by a process of carbonization—the hydrogen and minor volatiles turn to gas and escape, while the carbon becomes "fixed" and is retained for possible use as a fuel. Limestone when deposited by algae and other forms of life is also an organic rock.

Meteorites are especially interesting rocks. They come to the earth from outer space, presenting intriguing problems as to their origin and history. They are aggregates of minerals, both metallic and nonmetallic, much like certain terrestrial rocks, although they have distinctive features of their own. (See Chapter 12.)

Gems are minerals and rocks—and they also include a few animal and vegetable materials outside the limits of the mineral kingdom, as well as their man-made substitutes

—that are attractive enough to serve for personal adornment and other decoration. (See Chapter 8.)

The term stone has no scientific standing—we should be able, after a little study, to tell whether a particular bit of the mineral kingdom is a rock or a mineral. The word, however, does have a proper place, not only in literature and poetry, but also when the commercial usage of earth materials is referred to. Granite and marble are correctly called building stones or monument stones according to their use in construction or memorials; diamond and amethyst are two of the many gem stones; slate is a roofing stone.

## OUR MINERAL HERITAGE

The prosperity of modern man depends upon the natural resources at his disposal and the energy and intelligence that he applies to their utilization. The average family in the year 1800 lived, as far as material things were concerned, very much like the family of hundreds of years before. The incredible changes that have come about with such rapidity during the past one hundred and fifty years are due largely to the increased use of natural resources, especially minerals. The daily life of the average person has changed more during almost any twenty-five year period within that time than it did during the entire twenty-five centuries before, and the resources of the mineral kingdom are chiefly responsible, for good or ill, for this transformation.

Minerals in the industrial era have meant energy, tools, and the raw materials for manufacturing. The ultimate appearance of most minerals in industry is in the form of either chemicals or metals. These have made possible the production in quantity of the necessities of existence, including sufficient clothing and even food; the normal comforts and conveniences of present-day life, such as automobiles; and the luxuries—television, for instance—that add the rich touch to otherwise adequate living.

The economic geologist or mineral technologist who is

FIG. 1—World-wide mineral specimens. Left row (bottom to top): baddeleyite, Brazil; hematite, Elba; cassiterite, Bolivia; garnet, North Carolina; quartz, Brazil; right row: liquated stibnite; fluorite, England; quartz, Colorado. (*Photo by Victor Klepler, courtesy of Foote Mineral Co.*)

concerned with the finding, recovery, and processing of minerals divides them into three general groups according to their use—metallics, fuels, and nonmetallics.

First, there are the metallic minerals or *ores,* from which metals are extracted; they are discussed in Chapter 13. These may be precious metals, including gold, silver, and platinum; or base metals, such as copper and lead; or steel-making metals, such as iron and manganese. Many of the minerals that yield metals have a typically metallic luster, as does pyrite, but others, such as azurite, which is an ore of copper, give no hint that a metal can be taken from them, because they look earthy or glassy rather than metallic.

The mineral fuels belong to the second group of economic mineral products. Besides iron and copper, coal has occupied the most essential position in the mineral kingdom. Petroleum must now be added, so that the fuels, whose contribution is energy, are represented by two of the four earth substances most vital to an industrial economy. Natural gas is another important mineral fuel. All this energy has been stored in the rocks for long geologic ages and is being released at a rate that is viewed with alarm by thoughtful observers.

The third group of commercial minerals comprises the nonmetallic or so-called industrial minerals. Hundreds of them are used in thousands of ways. They are classified as nonmetallic because their use is without regard to the presence of any metal in them. Many such minerals do have one or more metals, commonly iron or aluminum, as part of their chemical formulas, but the physical characteristics rather than the metal content determine the use of these minerals. For instance, clay contains a large amount of aluminum, but the value of clay depends upon its becoming plastic when wet (a physical property) and has nothing to do with the aluminum in it. The best kind of asbestos, as another example, contains magnesium, a metal of growing importance; but the remarkable flameproof fibers that can be woven from asbestos (see page 208) do not depend for this quality upon the magnesium metal that is present.

The industrial minerals of this group cover a diverse list of applications. Structural materials for homes and other buildings include gypsum for plaster, limestone for cement, and asphalt for roofing. Abrasives for grinding and polishing run the gamut from diamond, the hardest mineral, to talc, the softest. Insulating materials to keep out heat, cold, and noise include a porous rock such as pumice and an expansible mineral such as vermiculite, which strangely swells to a large volume when "popped" (see page 216). Fertilizers--particularly phosphates, potash, and nitrates—replace depleted elements in the soil and greatly aid scientific farming. Ceramic materials such as clay make possible a wide variety of porcelain and pottery objects. And there are countless more—mineral pigments, gem stones, refractories, and many others.

With so large a share of human energy spent on war and preparation for war, the military uses of minerals can scarcely be overlooked. Modern weapons, whether flown in the air, wheeled on the ground, or carried by hand, are made mostly of metal. Ammunition, both of small arms and of artillery types—including projectile or missile, powder, and primer—is manufactured almost wholly from mineral substances. Explosives are compounded from sulfur and nitrates; bullets are made of lead, and cartridges of brass, an alloy of copper and zinc. It has been said with much justification that the "Allied cause floated to victory upon a wave of oil." The uranium minerals (Chapter 10) are the source of atomic power, with all its military implications.

Mining is one of the four basic industries that produce new wealth from the land and sea, the others being agriculture, fisheries, and lumbering. Mining, however, has come a long way from its humble and even accidental beginnings to its present stature.

The earliest mining evolved from the chance picking up of gold nuggets in shallow or dry stream beds. These, and pieces of other native metals, especially copper and silver, were used first as ornaments, since they are brightly colored and can easily be beaten into shape with stones. Beads and ear decorations of meteorites have been uncovered in prehistoric Indian mounds in Ohio. Besides such metals primitive peoples used gem stones not less than one hundred thousand years ago for their beauty and for the talismanic powers ascribed to them. The oldest form of mining was the systematic recovery of gems and decorative stones, and the first large-scale operation was at the turquoise deposits on the Sinai Peninsula, at least as early as 3400 B.C.

Flint, a kind of quartz, entered into widespread commerce as a most suitable material for weapons, which were the foundation of the first manufacturing industry. Native copper soon passed from an exclusively ornamental mineral to become a valuable metal for tools, utensils, and weapons.

Forest fires started by lightning were probably responsible for introducing man to the art of smelting, which was to revolutionize his life, making it possible for him to extract metals from otherwise worthless rock. Smelting also enabled him to mix together or alloy two or more metals. Such an alloy is bronze, a mixture of copper, tin, and zinc, which was produced in places as far apart as England and China, where ores containing the necessary metals are found near one another. Thus the Stone Age yielded to the Bronze Age.

Upon the heels of advancing technical skill with metals came the Iron Age. Occasional uses of native and meteoric iron are recorded, but the ores of iron give up their metal with great reluctance, so that it was not until long after copper, silver, tin, lead, and mercury were obtained in metallic form that iron could be smelted. The first production may have been by the Hittites as early as the thirteenth century B.C., and the process was well established in Greece by 1000 B.C. In a very real sense we are still living in the Iron Age.

The development of trade and transportation centered largely around mineral and gem products, those that were needed and those that were merely desired. An example of the former is salt, a mineral indispensable to life. The location of salt springs guided the flow of traffic through many a country. Cassiterite, the chief mineral of tin, was imported into Italy from Cornwall at least by the time of Caesar's conquest of Britain, and the Phoenicians obtained it much earlier from the nearby Scilly Islands or the coast of Spain. Amber is an example of a nonessential but highly prized substance, a gem which lured the Phoenician mariners of 1000 B.C. through the Pillars of Hercules to the shores of the Baltic.

# 2

# Prospecting and Mining

Hunting for mineral wealth is somewhat like stalking game. It can, for instance, be done in solitary fashion, haphazardly, with no intention of making it more than a sport or hobby. Many an amateur mineral collector keeps his weather eye open for a likely vein of ore while he looks for pretty specimens. Mineral-searching can also be done as a serious business by a lone man wanting to earn a living at it but having little to invest except time and effort. Nonmetallic minerals are particularly conducive to this sort of operation. Or it can be conducted as a large-scale enterprise by companies employing many men and using expensive equipment. The gold mines in the Johannesburg area have 350,000 workers in their 6,600 miles of tunnels laid with electric railroads.

Prehistoric man, the great adventurer, to whom all things of the earth were new and miraculous, probably accepted minerals and rocks as he found them and utilized them to the best of his meager knowledge. As his horizon expanded he began to cast about for more of the substances of the earth that were especially attractive or had proved to be useful to him. An early mineral-hunting expedition is the subject of the mythological story of the band of heroes who sailed with Jason in the Ship Argo to Colchis, seeking the Golden Fleece.

For over 2,000 years the Egyptian Pharaohs sent organized parties into the Sudan, the Sinai Peninsula, and the Arabian Desert to find and recover turquoise and emeralds. The discovery of new minerals intensified the interest of men

11

in all the various products of the mineral kingdom. This in turn led to a growing understanding of their occurrence and origin, eventually becoming the science of geology, which had its modern beginnings during the eighteenth century in the study of ores in the mines of Saxony.

## PROSPECTING

The prospector and his burro are symbols of the partnership of man and beast in the search for minerals. Grubstaked perhaps by a hopeful merchant who stands to share in the winnings, a few solitary figures of this dwindling breed still take to the hills in summer, or to the desert in winter, with a faithful animal for help and companionship. Countless are the romantic stories of bonanzas brought to light by such old-time prospectors and even by their burros, as recorded in the chapter of the American West that belongs to both of them.

**Early Prospecting.** The Bunker Hill and Sullivan mine, a silver-lead-zinc producer in the Coeur d'Alene district of Idaho, is one of the valuable mineral deposits popularly supposed to have been located by a lost burro. According to the story, when recaptured it was seen staring in apparent amazement at the bright reflection of a lead vein across the sunny canyon below Bunker Hill! Another tale that still survives is the one concerning Jim Butler's burro, credited with locating the outcrop of the Mizpah vein in the silver-and-gold camp of Tonopah, Nevada.

Rich mines have indeed been uncovered by accident. Cerro de Potosí, the hill of silver in Bolivia, is said to have begun to yield its wealth in 1544 when a llama uprooted the bush to which it was tied, disclosing a vein of native silver. The diamond fields of South Africa sprang into fame upon the discovery of the magnificent "Star of South Africa" by a shepherd boy in 1869. The Sudbury nickel district in Ontario had its birth in 1883 when a blacksmith working on a construction gang noticed shining yellow minerals in a railroad cut. The California gold rush started, and American history was changed, with the surprise appearance of a large flake of metal in the tailrace of Johann Sutter's sawmill on January 24, 1849. Inexperienced Nevada miners in 1859 washed the dirt thrown up by a ground squirrel and opened the Comstock lode where Virginia City now stands.

The badge of the prospector's profession was the gold pan. Often it served to fry bacon at a campfire after the day's work was done. A deft touch is needed to save the gold picked up by the pan, but this skill can be acquired with a little practice. Each piece of gold remaining at the bottom of the pan, after the lighter material has been washed over the side by repeated swirling and tipping, is called a color.

A gold miner in a new placer region follows the colors upstream, trying first one tributary and then another; as his recovery increases he knows that he is on the right track. If the gold suddenly ceases to show, he then realizes that he has passed the original vein that must have supplied the metal, and he begins to scour the slopes of the valley for it. Loose material on the surface, called float, serves as a clue to the nearby vein or "mother lode"; commonly the float consists of pieces of quartz riddled with rusty cracks. The most favorable site for a profitable deposit of gold, gems, or other placer minerals is in the slack water of an active stream along its middle reaches—especially where a swift stream surges out of a mountain valley onto a flat area, because there it must drop its treasure, which is too heavy for it to carry any farther.

The early prospector had a keen sense for gold and silver. True enough, he overlooked deposits of the many other metals that have been essential to modern life, but simply because he was not familiar with them. His knowledge of the telltale signs pointing to precious metal, however, amounted almost to instinct. These signs included recognition of the reddish, porous "iron hat" or gossan that often outcrops above buried veins of sulfide minerals, many of which carry gold or silver in appreciable quantity.

A doodlebug is any one of the many kinds of divining rods, dowsing rods, or witch sticks first used in medieval times to locate ores. Later such divining rods were applied to the finding of underground water. Many folks in rural areas still have unlimited faith in doodlebugs, though scientists are almost unanimous in condemning them. It is said that the inventor of the divining rod was hanged in Germany as a cheat and imposter.

**Modern Prospecting.** Man and machine have super-seded man and beast in the art of modern prospecting. Relying upon instruments based upon the rules of mathematics and the laws of physics, the trained prospector today uses a variety of methods to guide him in his quest. Such activity is often well organized, but there is plenty of room left for individuals seeking to "strike it rich" by uncovering a uranium deposit or the mother lode that forever beckons.

Air flights are now used for general reconnaissance, to get the lay of the land, to map the terrain, and to see where conditions seem to warrant detailed inspection on the ground. In remote parts of Canada prospectors in jeeps or canoes are supplied by aerial delivery. Geologic maps are carefully studied to check the spots that look favorable.

With the discovery of one mineral-bearing region after another, most of the places that reveal their existence by surface evidence have been eliminated, except perhaps in the uranium fields of Colorado, Utah, and adjoining states. Drilling holes into the earth is too costly to be done at random. Therefore many instruments have been devised to determine the rocks underground and decipher their structure. The methods that are applied are termed geophysical prospecting. More of this intensive (and expensive) type of scientific prospecting is done these days for petroleum than for metals.

Making use of the known physical characteristics of the earth's crust, the geophysicist, for example, measures the amount that the compass needle deviates from normal. About 1910 Thomas A. Edison designed a "magnetometer" for this purpose and prospected with it near Sudbury, Ontario, obtaining indications of ore at a spot that later developed into the rich Falconbridge mine. Delicate "airborne magnetometers" are even being carried over large areas by plane, and the results are later put on a map to show the magnetic attraction of the various rocks. Extensive new bodies of iron ore have been discovered in eastern Canada through this principle.

Another geophysical method records how the underlying rocks conduct or resist the flow of electricity through them. Ores buried beneath glacial debris have been located in this way in Sweden and Newfoundland. Metallic minerals generate natural currents of electricity; in other rocks, artificial currents are introduced into the ground. Magnetic and electrical properties are combined in various electromagnetic methods, which have proved themselves in frozen and desert regions.

Gravity methods of prospecting are based on the principle that dense rocks exert a greater pull of gravity than light rocks. The difference can be determined by the swinging of a pendulum, the twisting of a torsion balance, or the elastic springing of a gravimeter. These instruments are used mainly in the search for oil.

Still another geophysical method, called seismic exploration, involves the use of man-made earthquake waves, set up by exploding buried dynamite. The speed and direction of the waves, which are picked up by seismographs, reveal the density, elasticity, and depth of the rock layers through which they pass. Seismic methods have been particularly effective in the search for fuels and nonmetallic mineral deposits such as oil fields, coal beds, and salt domes.

Radioactivity in minerals and rocks can be detected with a Geiger counter, to be described in Chapter 10. Thousands of these sensitive instruments have been sold in battery-operated, portable models made especially for prospectors, who scour the countryside listening for the click of the earphone, which counts each gamma ray as it strikes the inner tube and causes a momentary discharge of electricity. In some models a light may flash instead, or a meter may register the strength of the radiation.

Geochemical prospecting is another recent development, which has gained stature through the success it has achieved in Finland and Russia. Mere traces of elements in soils, vegetation, and water often give valuable clues to hidden ore deposits. For instance, a certain kind of shrub, Viola calaminaria et zinci, tends to absorb zinc through its roots and so indicates the presence of zinc minerals in the rocks beneath; this zinc pansy grows profusely on waste ore dumps in the zinc-mining region of central Europe. Another kind of plant, Equisetum or horsetail, is said to concentrate gold in its seeds, suggesting the distinctly interesting possibility of harvesting a new crop every few years from your private gold farm.

## MINING

After a promising-looking mineral deposit has been discovered, prospecting gives way to mining. First, however, the deposit should be examined to estimate its potential value, and the most profitable manner of operating it should be decided upon.

**Mining the Land.** Placer mining is the simplest kind, requiring only the separation of one or more heavy minerals from the rest of the sand or gravel. Equipment may range from a forty-cent gold pan, through a variety of rockers, jigs, and sluice boxes that accomplish the same result on a large scale, to a million-dollar dredge. In the earlier days of California a particular form of placer mining called hydraulicking, in which the men resembled firemen more than miners, was commonly used. Powerful jets of water were directed upward at a bank of loose gravel, undermining it so that it collapsed and could be handled more conveniently. The same procedure is still employed in the tin mines of Burma; so strong and dangerous are the streams of water that issue from the nozzles that only the natives of certain districts, who are known for their phlegmatic temperament, are entrusted with the hoses, lest a worker kill a man by turning the blast on him in a fit of anger.

Dredges are floating mines. Picture a flatboat moving slowly on an artificial pond, excavating the ground ahead of it to a considerable depth below the water level, passing it back on an endless belt while the gold is being removed, and dumping the waste rock to fill the hole behind it. Thus the pond moves forward, carrying upon it the dredge which behaves like an earth-eating monster devouring his way through the soil. The enormous heaps of rejected rock that line the Sacramento River and other streams in California remind one of winding stacks of silver dollars when viewed from the air. In the Fairbanks district, the main gold producing region in Alaska, the frozen ground may require three years to thaw so that a small lake can be prepared for dredging.

Strip mining is a first cousin to dredging, but it takes place on dry land. Huge bulldozers or power shovels extract the overburden, which is the soil and barren rock overlying a flat bed of coal, clay, or other sedimentary deposit, in order to reach the lower layer of useful mineral. Often a shovel moves down parallel trenches, putting the waste rock from one strip back into the adjoining strip from which the valuable material had already been taken.

A quarry is a mine from which building stone, such as granite or marble, is obtained. Some quarries are shallow pits; others are openings that gradually extend horizontally into the side of a hill or cliff. The blocks of stone are usually taken out so as to leave steplike benches one above another. To avoid shattering the blocks while separating them, explosives are used moderately. Wedges are also pounded into holes drilled in hard rock, causing it to spring away from the wall. Softer rocks are often grooved with a channeling machine and then removed in smaller pieces. Wire saws, which are twisted steel cables fed with sand and water and run as an endless belt, have come to be more widely used in quarrying than any other method, especially in limestone and slate. The immense granite quarries at Barre, Vermont, are among the most impressive to be seen anywhere. In addition to building stone, quarries are also operated for other structural materials, such as gypsum and sand, and pegmatite minerals, such as feldspar and gems. Ores of a few metals, such as manganese, are also sometimes quarried.

A mineral body of large volume and low grade, lying on or near the surface, is likely to be mined as an "open cut," a single huge excavation exposed to the sky. The entire rock—ore and waste alike—is removed in a mass. Only in such a way can the cost be kept low enough to justify working such a meager deposit. The biggest mining operations in the world are of this kind, ranging from the deep diamond mines in South Africa to the huge so-called porphyry copper mines in the western states and Chile.

Some of these copper mines are so large that long freight trains look like model railroads as they spiral up the side of the pit from one great bench to the next, hauling the ore from the working level to the concentrating mills at the surface. The Utah Copper mine at Bingham Canyon is a stupendous opening which is being transformed from a mountain of ore into a bowl-shaped pit that will be 8,000 feet long, 6,000 feet wide, and 2,500 feet deep after the productive 580,000,000,000 tons of rock have been extracted. Open cuts also produce asbestos in Quebec, clay in Cornwall, England, aluminum ore in Arkansas, iron ore in the Lake Superior region, manganese ore in Russia, pyrite in Spain, and other mineral products elsewhere.

Sometimes an open cut becomes so deep or so steep that the rock cannot be removed at the top even by lifting it out with cables. To enable mining to continue, shafts are sunk alongside the pit, and the broken ore and waste rock are moved underground and brought up the shaft to the surface. The whole mine is then called a gloryhole. The Kim-

FIG. 2—Open pit at Utah Copper mine, Bingham Canyon, Utah. Terraced slope in background is 1,900 feet high. (*Photo by Ewing Galloway, courtesy of Copper and Brass Research Association.*)

berley diamond mine, which reaches a depth of nearly 4,000 feet, is a gloryhole well deserving the name.

Mark Twain, who had some experience with the exaggerations of miners and prospectors, defined a mine as a hole in the ground with a liar standing at the top. Even if this statement may not be exactly true of the men concerned, it faithfully describes a typical mine as being a downward opening into the earth. The mine is entered by means of a vertical or inclined shaft. The miners descend by ladders or are let down in elevators or in the same ore buckets that will later bring up the broken rock. In mountainous places a tunnel instead may be driven straight into the hill, perhaps following a vein inside; the miners walk into the mine or ride in ore cars that travel on rails.

At convenient distances from the top of the shaft, horizontal openings called levels are drilled to reach the ore. These are sometimes named but are usually given letters or numbers that indicate how deep they are; for example, the "200 level," "200-foot level," "level B," etc. Levels are drifts if they follow (or drift along) the vein; they are crosscuts if they intersect the general trend of the vein. The exact position of the ore is approached by digging upward (in raises) or downward (in winzes) from the various levels; a stope is the room or opening at the immediate spot where the ore is actually being excavated. "Country rock" is the term applied to unmineralized waste rock surrounding the ore. Sometimes the ore minerals seem to have permeated the country rock, leaving no sharp boundary and forming what are known as assay walls because they too yield some value, together with the vein itself.

Along the Gulf Coast in Texas and Louisiana, a sulfur mine and a sulfur well are the same thing. Until Herman Frasch invented his method of extracting native sulfur in liquid form, most of the world's supply of this essential industrial mineral had come from beds in Sicily. Within a few years after the introduction of the Frasch process in 1894, the United States took over from Italy the leadership in the sulfur trade and now produces about 90 per cent of the total native sulfur.

This sulfur occurs in enormous amounts in the cap rock which lies above the spectacular underground features known as salt domes. These are gigantic plugs of rock salt, some of them perhaps as much as 25,000 feet thick. There are about 300 such domes in the Gulf region. They seem to have been thrust upward thousands of feet from beneath as plastic masses of salt, penetrating the surrounding rock and pushing it aside. Above a dozen of the salt domes sulfur is found in commercial quantities; Sulphur Dome in Louisiana yielded a total of 9,412,165 tons before becoming depleted, though it covers only 75 acres. An even larger number of domes are associated with prolific pools of oil.

The Frasch process is simplicity itself. Three concentric pipes, each set within a larger pipe, are placed in a hole drilled into the ground. Superheated water is forced under pressure down the outer pipe, melting the sulfur. Hot compressed air is sent down the inner pipe, and it forces the red molten sulfur up the middle pipe to the surface, where it is collected in huge vats, in which it cools to the yellow solid form of sulfur.

**Mining the Ocean.** Long after the continents have been stripped of most of their useful minerals, the ocean will still hold great promise of wealth for those who learn to extract its incalculable mineral riches. To date the chief contribution of the ocean to man's material welfare has been its fisheries, but the same elements that are found in the rocks on land also occur in the waters of the sea, having arrived there from the land and accumulated there since the beginning of geologic time. The manner of combination, however, and the relative amounts are different. Copper, for instance, becomes concentrated in shellfish, iodine in kelp or sea weeds, and iron in hydrous iron-silicate minerals.

The ocean is a gold mine of prodigious proportions. An estimated 5,688,000 tons of metallic gold is either dissolved in it or has been taken up on the surface of marine organisms. Chemical methods of extracting the gold are known, but nothing anywhere near a commercial process has yet been invented.

In contrast, however, magnesium has been profitably removed from sea water. Though not a precious metal, as gold is, magnesium is one of the lightweight miracle metals that came into prominence during the Second World War. For structural purposes it is lighter than aluminum and it is the principal ingredient of incendiary bombs. A large plant at Freeport, Texas, has been built to take magnesium chloride from sea water; after this compound is melted, an electric current is passed through it, resulting in the pure metal.

The ocean yields still other useful substances. Most of the world's supply of bromine, used mainly in ethyl gasoline, comes from marine water taken off the shores of Texas and California. Calcium chloride, valuable for controlling dust and ice on roads and rails, is extracted from sea water.

More important than any of these, and indispensable to human life, is ordinary salt. Early man probably satisfied a large part of his need for this mineral by evaporating it from sea water, and some salt is recovered commercially in this way at the present time.

## MILLING, SMELTING, REFINING

After rocks and minerals have been mined, they are usually treated by various processes to fit them for further use in manufacturing or other industries. Such treatment includes mechanical concentration or mineral dressing, reduction, and refining. It ranges from merely sorting the desired material from the worthless stuff by hand to costly methods which require a large investment and involve many different steps. Except as applied to certain products, such as building stones, which may be trimmed but must not be damaged, the sequence of operations generally begins with a preliminary crushing and may be followed by a finer grinding to powder size.

Concentration or *milling* is the separation of the valuable constituents from the useless ones. Some earth materials are obtained directly in their finished form; native gold and silver and nonmetallic minerals such as gems and asbestos are typical of this group. Others need further treatment and may have to be concentrated in order to avoid the expense of shipping low-grade material long distances. For this reason most ores are run through a process that eliminates as much gangue as possible before the enriched ore minerals, called the concentrates, are sent to a smelter situated elsewhere.

Some mineral products undergo hand picking; they travel on a moving belt or sorting table, where workmen remove either the valuable or the waste material. Fluorescent zinc ores in New Jersey and wolfram ores in Nevada are selected in this manner under ultraviolet light.

Fibers of asbestos are concentrated through the use of strong suction fans which blow them away from the heavier waste rock and into collectors or settling chambers.

Other interesting methods of separation are also practiced. One of these is amalgamation, which is based upon the tendency for particles of gold and silver to adhere to mercury; the mercury is then vaporized by heat and recovered in order to be used again, while the precious metals remain behind. Another, even simpler, method utilizes an electromagnet to lift out iron ores and other magnetic minerals; magnetic wolframite (a tungsten mineral) is thus separated from nonmagnetic cassiterite (a tin mineral), which occurs with it. Heavy minerals can be separated from light ones by gravity concentration, using jigs or vibrating tables, which are mechanical improvements over the gold pan. A novel related method called sink-and-float uses a thick suspension of a powdered metallic mineral in water; this serves as an extra-heavy liquid, in which lighter minerals will float and still-heavier ones will sink.

It might seem impossible to reverse this arrangement and enable the heavy minerals to float instead. Nevertheless, this technique is the most widely used of all concentrating methods. Called flotation, it depends upon the fact that various minerals, when added to water to form a pulp, will adhere to a froth of chemical reagents, into which bubbles of air have been passed. Almost any desired mineral, even though it is the heaviest one present, can be made to float on an appropriate froth, while the rest of the minerals settle to the bottom.

Metals are obtained from their ores by several methods of reduction. The most general process is called *smelting*, which, as the word suggests, is the melting of ores in furnaces usually fueled by coke or natural gas. A flux is used to aid the melting. A glassy slag carrying the nonmetallic substances rises to the top, while the molten metal drops to the bottom of the furnace, where it is taken out at intervals and run into molds. A special procedure is needed for almost each kind of metal; some metals, such as zinc and mercury, volatilize and must be trapped by condensation. Other types of reduction employ liquids, such as cyanide to dissolve gold and silver, sulfuric acid to leach copper ores, and plain water to wash out Chilean nitrates.

The final step in treating ores is *refining*, which removes impurities from the metal. Some of these are impurities only in a chemical sense, for they are valuable in themselves— for example, the gold mixed with copper and the silver mixed with lead. Refining is done with fire, electricity, or chemicals. Lead is fire-refined to recover any silver that is present, whereas copper is treated electrolytically to obtain gold as a by-product.

# 3

# How to Identify Minerals

Every mineral differs from all the rest in chemical composition and atomic structure. Its chemical elements, their kind and arrangement, give the mineral its properties, which furnish us with the means of identifying the mineral.

Each known property serves either to identify a particular mineral or to eliminate other minerals as possibilities. At the beginning of the process of testing an unknown specimen, all minerals of similar appearance are under suspicion, but determining any definite property reduces immediately the long list of likely minerals to just one or a few.

## PROPERTIES OF MINERALS

Properties are the qualities and characteristics by which a mineral may be recognized and identified. Thus, coldness is a property of ice, salty taste is a property of halite or rock salt, and heavy weight is a property of platinum. Some properties of a mineral, such as its color, may be determined by mere observation; others require tests that vary from simple to difficult—perhaps scratching a mineral in order to learn its hardness, perhaps making involved chemical or X-ray examinations. Properties that depend upon the optical nature, cohesion, density, magnetism, and electricity of minerals, and can at the same time be determined rather easily, are described here.

Color. The rich and satisfying colors of minerals are surely among the chief reasons for their irresistible appeal. Even Paleolithic man utilized mineral pigments such as ochers, which are mixtures of iron oxides and clay.

Certain minerals, especially the metallic ones, have a fairly constant color no matter where they are found, because the color is inherent in the mineral and cannot be changed without destroying the substance itself. Azurite, a basic copper carbonate, is always blue, as its name suggests; malachite, having almost the identical chemical composition, is thoroughly green. The lead gray of graphite and molybdenite, the bright yellow of native sulfur and orpiment, and the coppery red of niccolite are among the distinctive and reliable colors that aid in the rapid identification of minerals. The cause of color in these instances is tied up with the necessary atomic structure of the mineral.

Exposure to the atmosphere, however, tends to alter the colors of minerals, so that they need to be broken apart in order to observe a fresh surface. The pale brass-yellow of pyrite darkens, somewhat concealing the original color. Marcasite, though it has the same chemical formula as pyrite, darkens more quickly. The most conspicuous example of such tarnishing is bornite, an important copper-iron sulfide; miners generally call it peacock ore and purple copper ore because the original bronze color gives way so soon to a variegated blue and purple, becoming almost black in a matter of months.

Most minerals vary in color as their chemical composition changes. When sphalerite is pure zinc sulfide, it is white, but when a small quantity of iron atoms have taken the place of an equal number of zinc atoms, the mineral is green or yellow, darkening to brown and black as the amount of iron increases. Sphalerite can contain about 18 per cent iron and still remain sphalerite.

Minor amounts of foreign elements, not necessary to the chemical formula, are termed impurities. A good many minerals owe their color to such impurities. The gem mineral corundum is an excellent example; when it is pure aluminum oxide, it is entirely colorless and may be called white sapphire, but traces of other metallic oxides furnish it with a wide range of colors. The vibrant red of ruby is produced by a little chromium oxide, whereas a few per cent of titanium make the splendid blue of sapphire. Fluorite is another example of a mineral that shows an astounding range of colors, some of which seem to be structural in origin, inasmuch as they can be modified by pressure, radium rays, and other means. Consequently, fluorite is found in such lovely hues as wine yellow, rose, sky blue, violet blue, and many more, often strikingly combined in different zones within the same specimen.

The mingling of light rays which interfere as they are reflected from thin films and crystal layers just beneath the surface of a mineral give rise to some spectacular color effects. The vivid sheets of blue and orange that sweep across the face of labradorite, a kind of feldspar first discovered in Labrador, and the unsurpassed play of rainbow colors that enliven opal are due to this cause.

So elusive is the "true" color of a mineral that it sometimes is not seen until the specimen is reduced to a powder. The most familiar example is hematite, which may be reddish brown, brownish black, or entirely black when viewed in solid form. When powdered, however, all hematite becomes a typical Indian-red color, so called because the American Indian used it to obtain material for his war paint. The word hematite, in fact, means bloodstone, referring to the color that is revealed upon crushing. This color of a mineral powder is known as its streak, for it is generally obtained by rubbing the mineral on a piece of unglazed porcelain or streak plate. A rough white tile or a shattered piece of china will serve the same purpose. Even the steely-gray hematite found on the island of Elba and at Cumberland, England, and carved into warrior designs for men's rings will show the same reddish-brown streak. Limonite, a hydrous iron oxide, consistently shows a yellowish-brown streak, though its solid color may be dark brown or black. A number of minerals have a streak similar to their ordinary color but paler. Thus cinnabar, a vivid red mercury sulfide, has a scarlet streak; realgar, a red arsenic sulfide, has an orange-red streak; and blue azurite and green malachite have light-blue and light-green streaks, respectively.

**Luster.** The appearance of the surface of a mineral in reflected light is known as its luster. This property is not easy to separate from color, for they are intimately related and we tend to think of them together. We speak, for instance, of chalcopyrite as having a brass-yellow color and magnetite an iron-black color, these being very different from the yellow of sulfur and the black of biotite mica. The two properties are especially difficult to consider apart from each other in sphalerite; this most important of all zinc minerals is said to have a resinous luster, but at the same time it usually has the brownish color of a resin.

In spite of this confusion—and also because it is so obvious a property that it is rarely neglected—luster is very useful in recognizing and classifying minerals. By dividing all minerals into two groups on the basis of their luster, a simple method is provided for running down the identity of an unknown mineral, which can immediately be placed in one group or the other. These groups are called *metallic* and *nonmetallic*. The former does not need to be defined, except to say that it includes the minerals that have the luster of a typical metal—brass, bronze, aluminum, silver, and the rest. Some minerals have a *submetallic* luster which is somewhat glassy-metallic but hard to describe; to become familiar with it, a good specimen of columbite or wolframite should be examined.

To report the luster of a mineral as nonmetallic is still not sufficient to describe it, because there are a number of kinds of nonmetallic lusters. They are not difficult to learn, for most of them are named according to some common object that reflects light in a similar way. A *silky* luster, for example, is shown by fibrous minerals, such as asbestos and fibrous varieties of calcite, barite, and gypsum (known as satin spar). A *pearly* luster is found on talc, brucite, and other minerals that are foliated and easily cleaved (see page

31) . A *greasy* luster is shown by nepheline, a white silicate mineral formed in igneous rocks that do not contain enough silica to yield feldspar. Two other terms may need the help of definitions to be clear—*vitreous,* meaning glassy, and *adamantine,* meaning diamondlike. The most common luster among minerals is vitreous, which is characteristic of ordinary glass, as well as of quartz crystals and of hundreds of other minerals. The adamantine luster belonging to diamond is also shown on certain lead minerals, including cerussite (lead carbonate) and anglesite (lead sulfate) .

**Hardness.** Various objects may differ not only in the degree of hardness they possess, as everyone knows, but also in the kind of hardness. Diamond, for example, is the hardest of all known substances in the sense that only another diamond can scratch it, but a sharp blow will cause it to split readily along definite planes of weakness. Jade, on the other hand, can be scratched by a piece of quartz, yet its matted structure gives it an extraordinary resistance to breakage. A recent newspaper story told of a Chinese jeweler in San Francisco who was still using a jade anvil that had been in his family for three generations. Again, grains of quartz, each moderately hard in themselves may be so loosely cemented together in a sandstone that the rock can be crumbled in one's hand and is scarcely to be thought of as hard. Industrial tests for hardness measure resistance to abrasion or indentation, according to the sort of information that is desired. Strangely—though this has only a theoretical significance—hardness is perhaps one property that cannot ever be precisely determined, because the very act of testing for it presses against the atoms, causing them to close ranks so that the substance becomes even harder.

Scratch-hardness is the kind of hardness by which minerals are identified, whereas the resistance that the atoms offer to being separated in other ways is called toughness or tenacity. Some minerals, such as quartz, are *brittle,* breaking or powdering easily. A few, including argentite and cerargyrite (both silver minerals) are *sectile* and can be cut into shavings with a knife. Some, such as native iron, can be pounded thin and so are *malleable*. Native copper and silver are among the minerals that, besides being malleable, are also *ductile* and can be drawn into wire. Others, such as chlorite, are *flexible* and will bend. Still others, notably mica, are *elastic* and will spring back into position when released. Hardness and toughness together are called *cohesion*, which is the force of electrical attraction existing between the atoms that constitute the mineral.

About one hundred years ago a German mineralogist named Friedrich Mohs proposed the scale of hardness that bears his name. Designating diamond, the hardest mineral, as number 10, and talc, the softest mineral (it is crushed to make talcum powder) as number 1, he arranged the following table:

10 Diamond
9 Corundum
8 Topaz
7 Quartz
6 Feldspar
5 Apatite
4 Fluorite
3 Calcite
2 Gypsum
1 Talc

This scale simply means that a mineral can scratch any other listed below it, and can in turn, be scratched by all those above it. It indicates the rank, not the amount of hardness—that is, number 9 (corundum) is not three times as hard as number 3 (calcite); nor is diamond (number 10) twice as hard as apatite (number 5). Actually, the difference between the top two minerals is far greater than the range of the rest of the scale altogether. Quartz (number 7) is often considered as marking the division between the hard and soft minerals.

A set of minerals, corresponding to Mohs' scale and

known as hardness points, is handy to use for testing hardness. Also, certain common objects are suitable for approximating the hardness of minerals: the fingernail (considered as $2\frac{1}{2}$ and able to scratch gypsum), a copper cent (3), a brass pin (slightly over 3 and can scratch calcite), window glass ($5\frac{1}{2}$), a good knife blade (6), and a hardened steel file ($6\frac{1}{2}$).

In discussion of hardness, kyanite should be mentioned prominently. This remarkable mineral varies so much in its resistance to abrasion that it can be deeply gouged by a knife as it moves along the "grain," which runs the length of the crystal, but the same blade slips harmlessly over the surface in other directions.

Calcite is more constant, though a basal face on a crystal comes only to 2 on Mohs' scale; this is the less forgivable because calcite is supposed to set a standard as number 3. Other difficulties, such as the crumbling nature of a specimen or the lack of a fresh surface, may also make the hardness test unreliable.

**Cleavage.** Crystalline substances, as are most minerals, are composed of atoms arranged in definite layers in a three-dimensional pattern called a lattice, in which they are held together by electrical attraction (see page 51). In many minerals the cohesion is conspicuously weaker in certain directions than in others, and pressure or a blow will cause the mineral to split along the "grain," yielding smooth, flat surfaces. This property is known as cleavage.

Two factors, quality and direction, are used to describe cleavage. Thus "perfect octahedral" cleavage, typical of fluorite and diamond, is quickly produced parallel to the octahedron faces of isometric crystals (see page 110). An "indistinct prismatic" cleavage gives a somewhat obscure surface parallel to a prism face. Cleavage always operates along a possible face of a crystal, even if this particular face did not happen to grow on the specimen.

The prize-winning example of cleavage, so evident that no one could disregard it, is in mica. The flakes of muscovite or biotite mica can be peeled apart until they become invisible. Calcite has a splendidly developed cleavage which results in rhomb-shaped fragments; no matter how small the pieces are, each tiny particle will have the same form and exactly the same angles. The perfect octahedral cleavage of diamond enables the cutter to remove flawed or excess parts in a fraction of the time required to saw the crystal in any other direction. The identification of some important minerals is greatly facilitated by recognizing their characteristic cleavage patterns.

The term cleavage is often applied to rocks as well as to minerals and other crystals. However, this meaning is much less specific, referring only to the tendency of layered rocks to split into rough slabs.

**Fracture.** The breakage of a mineral or rock without any definite direction is known as fracture. It is described according to the appearance of the surface, using common words such as splintery, fibrous, irregular, uneven, even, and earthy. A *hackly* fracture is the kind seen on native copper and other metals which break with jagged edges. The most distinctive fracture is called *conchoidal,* meaning shell-like, because it resembles the concentric arcs on shells. Quartz and obsidian show conchoidal fracture especially well, as does ordinary chipped glass.

**Specific Gravity.** We say that iron is heavier than wood, yet we know that a large log will weigh more than a small lump of iron. We must be speaking, therefore, not about any piece of iron or wood, but about equal sizes of the two materials. It has become customary, because it is so convenient, to compare the weight of a substance with that of water. At 4 degrees centigrade, water is at its heaviest, a cubic centimeter of it weighing 1 gram. The relative density of other substances—whether solids, liquids, or gases— is expressed in terms of water at $4°$ C. and is known as the specific gravity of the substance. The specific gravity of a mineral might be defined as its weight divided by the weight of an equal volume of water. Thus, a specimen of sulvanite from Burra-Burra, Australia, having a specific gravity of 4.00 weighs four times as much as water, and diamond (specific gravity 3.52) weighs slightly more than three and one-half times as much. Fortunately, it is not necessary to calculate the volume of a specimen in order to determine its specific gravity.

Although all known gases under normal earth conditions, as well as most liquids, are lighter than water, minerals and rocks are all heavier than water. Still, they seem to weigh less in water than they do in air, in the same way as does a swimmer, who is buoyed up by a force equal to the amount of water that he displaces. This displaced water weighs as much as the solid body loses when it is submerged. Archimedes, the learned Greek mathematician and inventor, is supposed to have found this out when he stepped into a bath and observed the overflow of water, thereby discovering a way to determine whether King Hieron's gold crown was actually cheapened with silver.

The specific gravity of gems, minerals, and rocks is commonly determined by making two weighings. The formula to be used is simply the weight of the specimen in air, divided by the loss of weight when suspended in water. For example, a piece of rock may weigh 6 ounces in air and 4 ounces in water; the difference of 2 is divided into the original reading of 6 and the specific gravity comes out as 3.

Homemade equipment can give entirely adequate results for most purposes. Some sort of *beam balance,* with weights distributed along a horizontal arm, is especially suitable. Mineralogists often use a manufactured *Jolly balance,* which is fitted with a spring that stretches in proportion to the weight of the specimen placed in a pan at the bottom. A *pycnometer* is a small bottle that measures the amount of water that is lost after a specimen has been put into it. *Heavy liquids* are easy to use to identify gems and also to separate loose mineral grains according to their specific gravities. Pure bromoform, for instance, has a specific gravity of 2.89, so that genuine topaz sinks in it while yellow quartz of similar appearance floats. Valuable minerals found in sand are also heavy enough to sink in bromoform, whereas ordinary quartz and feldspar stay at the top. A fairly wide range of specific gravity is possible when several such liquids are mixed together, although a few of them are rather dangerous to handle.

The heaviest products of the mineral kingdom are the native metals. Osmium, a member of the platinum group, would have a specific gravity of 22.69 if it were found in a pure state, but all six of the platinum metals are always more or less alloyed with one another. Natural (impure) platinum reaches as high as 19.00, and platiniridium has been found up to 22.84. Gold without admixed silver is 19.31, while silver alone is 10.50. Liquid mercury has the astonishing value of 13.60.

The average mineral with a metallic luster may be regarded as having a specific gravity of slightly over 5, about the same as pyrite and hematite, the two most abundant metallic minerals. Consequently, the native metals mentioned above are quickly felt to be excessively heavy. A metallic-looking mineral that is much below average, such as graphite (2.23), seems unnaturally light to the touch because so much more weight is expected.

Nonmetallic minerals are likewise compared with average minerals of their own kind. The most common of these are quartz, feldspar, and calcite, which fall between 2.59 and 2.76. In contrast barite, at 4.30 to 4.60, is noticeably heavy, and ulexite, at 1.65, is conspicuously light. The heavy nonmetallic minerals include many that contain lead somewhere in the chemical formula though not resembling a metal in their surface luster. Other exceptionally heavy nonmetallic minerals are montroydite (11.22) and uraninite (10.63). Perhaps the lowest specific gravity among minerals is 1.48, recorded for oxammite from the Guanape Islands of Peru, and for crystals of sassolite, which is natural boric acid from Italy.

It is apparent that the specific gravity of a mineral depends both upon the kinds of elements present and upon the way in which they are held together. Lead minerals are heavy because lead is a heavy element, and hence lead carbonate (cerussite) has a higher specific gravity than calcium carbonate (calcite). However, aragonite has the same chemical formula as calcite, though it is about nine per cent heavier because the atoms are closer together.

**Magnetism.** A sufficiently strong source of magnetism produced by an electromagnet will influence many minerals, especially those containing iron, cobalt, or nickel. Some other minerals are also attracted and some are even repelled by a very strong magnet. However, only two common minerals, magnetite and pyrrhotite, are capable of being picked up by an ordinary steel magnet. Magnetite, an iron oxide, is, in fact, so named because of this property. The loadstone variety of magnetite is much more remarkable, being itself a natural magnet which will attract steel objects. Pyrrhotite, a bronze-colored iron sulfide, is less actively affected than magnetite. Some varieties of native platinum, containing iron, are also magnetic and may even be natural magnets.

**Electricity.** The word electricity comes from *elektron,* the Greek name for amber. Though a product of the vegetable rather than the mineral kingdom, being a fossil resin, amber is a gem and so is appropriately discussed here. The ancients found that amber when rubbed picks up tiny bits of various materials, such as paper and lint. This is not, however, a reliable test to distinguish amber from a mineral substitute or from its plastic or glass imitations. All minerals —especially diamond, topaz, and tourmaline—become electrified by friction but generally to a lesser degree than amber.

Electricity is produced in other ways besides friction. Tourmaline, for example, develops *pyroelectricity* when heated, becoming positive and negative at opposite ends, the poles reversing themselves upon cooling. Because of this property, tourmaline attracts dust as the temperature changes. When pressure instead of heat causes this "polar" electricity, the resulting effect is called *piezoelectricity;* being sensitive to slight differences in pressure, tourmaline is used in submarines to register electrically the depth of submergence. This procedure can be reversed by applying an alternating current to tourmaline and getting a change of volume so rapidly that it vibrates at a high frequency. Plates of quartz are used in the same way to control the frequency of radio broadcasts. Exposing fluorite and some other minerals to short radiation also produces an electrical condition, which is called *photoelectricity.*

## HABITS OF MINERALS

Minerals, like people, have certain habits which help to determine their character. These habits are not the same as the physical properties we have discussed; they are the tendencies of minerals to develop in particular ways, in response to factors such as temperature, pressure, and the nature of

Fig. 3—Cockscomb marcasite of unusual beauty from Cardin, Oklahoma, in the Tri-state district. (*Photo by Katherine H. Jensen, courtesy of Ward's Natural Science Establishment.*)

the mineralized solutions. For example, some minerals always tend to grow into mathematically accurate crystal forms (to be described in Chapter 7) or they may have a habit of growing into crystalline aggregates having a special over-all shape and appearance. In short, it is the "habit" of given minerals to grow in typical ways, either independently or in groups.

Many mineral habits are imitative. The most familiar are probably those of the stone icicles or *stalactites* found in caves. These are represented by 71 substances, including 67 minerals. Calcite and aragonite—two calcium carbonate minerals of the same chemical composition but different internal structure—are by far the most abundant of these. Calcite usually develops into compact and stumpy masses, occasionally of enormous size. Aragonite is more elongated and may present delicately radiating flowerlike growths. Some, called helictites, defy the law of gravity, twisting and turning upward and sideways in erratic fashion. Interlacing stems of snow-white aragonite appear somewhat like coral and are designated flos-ferri. Related bodies built up instead from the floor of a cave by dripping water are stalagmites. Marble Caves in Oregon contains noteworthy examples of pillars consisting of a stalactite and a stalagmite joined together. All such cavestone or dripstone is the result of the evaporation of percolating underground water, which deposits mineral matter formerly dissolved in it.

Orange-colored chalcedony quartz is found in the vicinity of Cisco, Utah, in aggregates of globules that resemble a bunch of grapes, and the specimens are called grape-stone. This habit is known as *botryoidal,* meaning "cluster of grapes." Limonite and goethite (hydrous iron oxides) also occur with botryoidal habit; and so does a variety of the tin oxide, cassiterite, which is called woodstone because of its brown color and fibrous structure.

Still larger rounded masses are termed *reniform* because they resemble kidneys. Handsome black specimens of hematite from Cumberland, England, have this habit. Even larger curved masses of hematite, malachite, and other minerals are called *mammillary* from their breastlike size and shape.

The *acicular* habit is that of needlelike crystals. Bright brown needles of rutile are often enclosed in quartz, where they are sometimes known as Cupid's arrows. The whole specimen is named rutilated quartz. Tourmaline, hornblende, actinolite, and other minerals are also found in this distinctive habit and occurrence.

A *fibrous* habit is typical of asbestos, satin spar (a silky variety of gypsum), and other minerals having many closely parallel fibers and a silky luster. Some kinds of calcite, barite, and jamesonite ("feather ore") are clearly fibrous.

*Capillary* minerals are also stretched-out crystals, but they curl in hairlike forms. The fiery red hairs of cuprite, called chalcotrichite, are among the most eagerly sought of all minerals. This copper oxide has never been common, and the difficulty of preserving it, owing to its fragile condition, has helped to make it even scarcer. Some of the zeolite minerals, found in cavities in basaltic lava, are likewise capillary; some specimens, twisted and matted together like felt, are called *filiform,* such as the "cotton-stone" mesolite from the Scottish Isle of Skye.

Elongated crystals flattened like a knife blade are called *bladed.* Lovely blue pieces of kyanite from St. Gothard, Switzerland, have this habit. With its translucent or transparent blue center and white margins, and its pearly luster, kyanite is a most attractive mineral. Beautiful green crystals of kyanite come from Yancy County, North Carolina.

A *tabular* habit refers to a book or table shape, much thinner in one dimension (thickness) than in width and length. Rhodocrosite and wollastonite are recognized as tabular minerals, the latter being known also as tabular spar.

*Prismatic* minerals, such as arfvedsonite, are pencil-shaped, and *columnar* minerals, such as some hornblende, occur in stout columns or drawn-out blocks.

Flattened crystals that branch out like trees or ferns are called *dendritic* or *arborescent*. Jack Frost traces such patterns with ice on the window pane. Manganese oxide and sometimes iron oxide spread out to paint this design on surfaces of limestone or sandstone and in moss agate—which does not contain any moss at all, either plant or fossil. This pattern does, however, preserve in stone an eternal landscape, with realistic scenes of mountain and lake, coast and forest, park and stream. Crystals of metals, including gold, silver, and copper, are often handsomely dendritic.

A *reticulated* habit shows a latticelike network of crystals crossing one another at definite angles. Cerussite, a bright white carbonate of lead, is the most familiar and attractive mineral answering to this description.

*Rosettes* are concentric groupings of crystals, individual plates of which are arranged like the petals of a rose. When occurring like this, hematite is called "iron rose," gypsum and quartz are called "desert rose," and barite is called "barite rose." The last-named mineral can be picked up by the thousands near Norman, Oklahoma.

Crystals radiating in all directions from a common center and producing starlike forms are said to be *stellated*. Shiny green stars of wavellite from Magnet Cove, near Hot Springs, Arkansas, are among the finest of this type.

Surfaces that are covered with a myriad of closely set tiny crystals are said to be *drusy*. Quartz is the most common mineral of this kind. Blue drusy quartz from Globe and other copper camps in Arizona makes sparkling specimens. Drusy crystals are numerous inside geodes, which are mineral-lined concretions in sedimentary rocks. The inner surface of the geode shell is often covered with layers representing successive stages of deposition of agate and other minerals which have settled out of solution. Crystals are likely to be implanted upon this solid base and project into the open interior. The small bright crystals nestling among larger ones aptly fit John Ruskin's description of "courtier crystals glittering in attendance upon others." The magnificent amethyst geodes from Brazil and Uruguay enclose symmetrically formed and exquisitely colored crystals of purple quartz. Geodes weighing hundreds of pounds have been recovered from the prolific gem areas in those countries. Some geodes are quite irregular, perhaps constricted into tortuous shapes. Even when rounded or ellipsoidal, they are usually rough on the outside. A geode may look like an ordinary concretion, but inside is a treasure cave of beautiful crystals and other gemmy material.

Minerals that separate easily into leaves or scales, as does brucite from the Shetland Islands, are said to be *foliated*. Such a separation, carried to a state of extreme thinness, is called *micaceous;* it is inherent in the members of the mica group of minerals, described on page 73.

Two terms of a more general nature are used to describe the habit of minerals. *Granular* refers to aggregates of coarse or fine grains of no particular shape, and *massive* indicates compact material without any peculiar or imitative form.

## BLOWPIPE TESTS

The relatively simple blowpipe method of identifying minerals involves chemical and physical tests with a blowpipe, chemical reagents, and other modest items of equipment. Knowing the properties of minerals (as already described) and being able to find them conveniently arranged in books and tables reduce this sort of mineral identification to a matter of systematic procedure.

A blowpipe is merely a metal tube for blowing a narrow jet of air into a flame. Elaborate equipment can be used, but it is not likely to give any more satisfactory results than an inexpensive blowpipe and a gas burner. Their skillful manipulation is usually mastered readily, even though it requires breathing in through the nose and out through the mouth at the same time, while maintaining a constant supply of air in the cheeks. This is really very easy!

**Flame.** The cone-shaped flame created by the action of the blowpipe is pointed in a horizontal direction, like a pennant waving in a breeze. It consists of three parts—an inner blue zone of unburned gas mixed with air; a pale violet middle zone of burning gas, moisture, and carbon monoxide; and an invisible outer zone of air, moisture, and carbon dioxide. This hot outer part of the flame is spoken of as the oxidizing flame, because enough air is present to add oxygen to any mineral that wants it, as happens when native copper becomes coated with copper oxide. The zone next inside is called the reducing zone, because its carbon monoxide searches out any available oxygen, even removing oxygen from heated minerals containing it, as when copper oxide is changed to metallic copper.

The blowpipe process is vastly simplified by dividing minerals at the start into two major groups according to whether they have a metallic or a nonmetallic luster. The minerals that show a distinctly colored streak, such as azurite and cinnabar, are considered to be metallic.

Further subdivision is then made on the basis of other essential physical properties, such as color, hardness, cleavage, and specific gravity.

Tests for gold, silver, tin, lead, and copper can be made by heating on a block of charcoal any mineral that contains these metals. The reducing flame of the blowpipe melts the mineral, extracts oxygen and other volatiles, and brings out the actual metal as a yellow ball of gold, a red mass of copper, a gray piece of bismuth, a gray globule of lead, or a white sphere of silver or tin. If iron, or nickel, or cobalt is also present, the resulting product of this treatment will be magnetic.

Some metals and other elements, when similarly heated, vaporize and then settle onto the charcoal as sublimates or coatings in different positions and various colors; they can also be distinguished from one another by their reactions when further treated chemically. Lead minerals, for instance, give a white or pale yellow deposit which turns canary yellow when a mixture of potassium iodide and sulfur is added. Bismuth minerals give a bright red deposit with the same chemicals.

**Bead Tests.** Bead tests are made by melting some borax or a similar flux in a loop at the end of an iron, nichrome, or platinum wire (previously inserted in the end of a glass rod) and fusing a little of the powdered mineral in the bead thus formed. Chromium minerals give a clear green bead, cobalt minerals a deep blue, and other metals still other distinctive colors, depending upon the flux used, the amount of mineral powder, the type of flame (whether oxidizing or reducing), and the temperature—the color changes when the bead cools. The various possible combinations that are obtained help us to identify the particular mineral.

**Flame Colors.** Characteristic colors are also secured by strongly heating minerals that contain certain elements. Held in a flame, either in forceps or on a platinum wire, these minerals volatilize and glow vividly in many hues. The strontium in celestite, for example, gives forth a glorious crimson, the barium in barite is yellow green, and the copper in bornite is emerald green or azure blue according to whether it appears as an oxide or a chloride. The cheerful colors of pine cones prepared for holiday fireplaces are made in similar fashion. The blue glow of old driftwood burned at campfires was due to copper chloride resulting from the reaction between copper nails and salt from the sea. Other flame colors include the purplish red of lithium, as in petalite, the orange red of calcium, as in aragonite, and the yellowish green of boron, as in colemanite. Even the slightest trace of sodium gives a strong yellow that persists almost indefinitely and is hard to get rid of; it so hides the pale violet color caused by potassium that a blue glass is needed to filter it out.

**Open Tube.** Minerals are heated in a hollow glass rod to give so-called open tube tests. Thus antimony minerals, such as stibnite, when heated in this way give off a dense white gas of antimony oxides, which are so heavy that they may be rocked back and forth in the tube before they settle on the glass as a yellow powder, which cools white. Gray metallic globules of mercury are formed when mercury minerals are heated in this way. Lighter gases, such as arsenic oxide, rise in the tube and settle on the sides farther up; or they may escape entirely, as sulfur does when it turns to sulfur dioxide.

**Closed Tube.** When an open tube is melted shut at one end, it becomes a closed tube, in which many minerals give typical reactions. Water in a hydrous mineral, for instance, such as gypsum, will vaporize and condense into drops inside the tube. A mineral carrying much sulfur, such as pyrite, will leave a red sublimate of sulfur that turns yellow as it cools. Arsenic sulfide, as in realgar, deposits a dark red liquid which changes to a reddish yellow solid upon cooling. Other elements and compounds give individual reactions in their own way.

**Chemical Tests.** The elements or groups of elements of which minerals are composed may also be identified by various tests with acids and other reagents. One such test of especial beauty is for nickel; it is described, as applied to meteorites, on page 175. Rocks containing phosphorus are identified by moistening them with nitric acid and applying ammonium molybdate solution, which turns the specimens a canary yellow color. This is a useful test to know about, inasmuch as valuable phosphate rocks look like any ordinary rock in the field.

When a mineral containing silver is dissolved in nitric acid, the slightest addition of hydrochloric acid results in the immediate formation of a white cloudy precipitate of silver chloride. Conversely, the presence of chlorine in a mineral, such as halite, can be shown by adding silver nitrate to the solution and getting the same white clouds.

Carbonate minerals all effervesce in acid, evolving carbon dioxide gas, as explained on page 58. If a mineral is dissolved in acid, and common household ammonia or ammonium hydroxide is then added to the solution, a deep blue color indicates copper in the mineral, a pale blue color means nickel, a white fluffy precipitate suggests aluminum, and a brown fluff points to iron. (Details of these and many other interesting and worthwhile tests are given in the books on mineral identification described on page 243.)

Few minerals can be identified by a single blowpipe or chemical test, but cassiterite, the chief source of tin, is a prominent exception. Fragments of cassiterite, which often occur as stream pebbles, are placed in hydrochloric acid with a piece of zinc metal; hydrogen is set free, and this gas combines with oxygen on the outside of the cassiterite, leaving a surface coating of metallic tin which can be polished bright by rubbing it briskly. No other natural substance acts in this manner.

It is often necessary to distinguish between two minerals that closely resemble each other. A pair of such minerals are graphite and molybdenite; both are gray and soft enough to mark paper, but molybdenite alone gives the sulfur test mentioned above. Rhodonite and rhodochrosite are two pink manganese minerals, but only the latter effervesces when touched with acid. Anhydrite and gypsum look much alike, but gypsum releases water when heated, which anhydrite does not do. Numerous other minerals of similar appearance exist that can be separated on the basis of a single test.

## X–RAY IDENTIFICATION

More intricate methods of identification make use of optical examinations with a petrographic microscope, and quantitative chemical analyses which determine the proportions of the elements that are present. The ultimate precision in identifying most crystalline minerals is accomplished by means of X-ray photography, which gives a specific pattern corresponding to the atomic structure of the mineral. Investigations along this line began in 1912 when Max F. F. von Laue advanced the proposition that the atoms in crystals might be spaced at the right distance to diffract X-rays in the same way that a ruled grating diffracts rays of light. Experimental proof was promptly forthcoming and a new era in the study of minerals began.

A *Laue diffraction pattern* shows the general internal symmetry of crystals in wonderful perfection. Precise measurements of structure are made possible by the so-called *rotation method* or one of its modifications. Minerals and other crystals can be accurately identified by the *powder method*, for which only a small amount of powdered material is needed. A series of concentric circles appears as short arcs on a narrow strip of photographic film. These are compared, like fingerprints, with pictures of known patterns, using code numbers to find the film of the identical crystal already filed away.

4

# How Minerals Are Classified

Because there are numerous ways to classify minerals, the choice lies in the purpose that will be served. By combining similar characteristics and showing the relationships among them, many different arrangements are possible. The early observers of minerals grouped them according to their appearance—by color and luster and sometimes by the uses to which the minerals were put, much as we would still do today if we did not have more adequate means of testing them. In his *Book of Stones,* the first textbook on mineralogy (about 315 B.C.) Theophrastus, who was a pupil of Aristotle, divided 16 minerals into "metals, stones, and earths." By A.D. 1556 Agricola had enlarged this classification only to the extent of "earths, salts, gem stones, and other minerals," although he was familiar with many more minerals than Theophrastus. The rigidly scientific classifications of the present day are valuable in helping us to study and understand the true nature of minerals.

Scientific mineral classifications have had many changes since the first "modern" one, the *Systema Naturae* of Carolus Linnaeus, published in 1735. It was a chemical type, as were succeeding classifications by Wallerius and Cronstedt. The principles of crystallography were added to those of chemistry by Rome de l'Isle in 1772. Many of the other outstanding eighteenth and nineteenth century pioneers in mineralogy devised their own classifications. Chief among these were the arrangements of Werner, Mohs, and Dana.

Abraham Gottlob Werner's widespread influence in mineralogy stemmed from his fame as a teacher at the mining academy in Freiberg, Saxony. His classifications, based on the external character and physical properties of minerals, were altered from time to time by his students.

Friedrich Mohs based his classification upon the crystallography of minerals, and he endeavored to elucidate the confusing accumulation of variety names by giving emphasis to the mineral species.

James D. Dana, in the first edition (1837) of his *System of Mineralogy*, revised Mohs' method and added the chemical relationships known to exist between the species. Further concessions to the growing influence of chemistry were made in the second edition (1844), and by the time of the third edition (1850) the chemical composition of minerals took precedence over the crystallography. Varieties were restored in the fifth edition (1868), in which the classification was based upon a combination of chemistry, crystallography, and physical properties. This method has prevailed to the present time.

The seventh edition of *Dana's System of Mineralogy* (by Palache, Berman, and Frondel) has classified minerals according to the new science of *crystal chemistry,* which is based upon the X-ray analysis of mineral structure, and which unites crystallography and chemistry even more intimately than before.

## THE COMPOSITION OF MINERALS

Minerals, like all other substances in the physical world, are composed of atoms. Since they combine in countless ways to make up every known sort of material, atoms have been referred to as the "building blocks of the universe." Each different kind of atom is called a chemical element; there was believed to be a total of 92 possible elements (from hydrogen to uranium) until the research work which led to the utilization of nuclear energy was begun and new elements began to be produced artificially. An atom is the smallest fraction of any element that can exist by itself and still show the chemical qualities of that particular element.

For example, one atom of carbon is the least amount of carbon that can have the chemical characteristics necessary to this element.

Atoms, we now know, are complicated things. They have some parts with obscure relationships, and other parts that apparently can be assembled in a variety of ways and can even change from one kind into another. The descriptive, nonmathematical view of an atom is that it rather resembles the solar system, with negative charges called electrons revolving in wavelike fashion in approximate orbits around a nucleus, somewhat like planets around the central sun, but held in their paths by electrical attraction. The simplest idea of the nucleus is that it consists of two main types of particle, each weighing over 1,800 times as much as an electron. These particles are protons, which are charged positively (to the same extent as the electrons are charged negatively), and neutrons, which have no electrical charge at all. The sum of the weights of the protons and neutrons in the nucleus is the atomic weight of the element. Ordinary oxygen has a relative atomic weight of 16, and the other elements are compared to this standard value.

The atomic number of an element, however, is the same as the number of protons in the nucleus. This is always equal to the number of electrons that revolve around the nucleus, in order that the positive and negative charges will balance. Furthermore, and very important, the atomic number of an element determines the chemical properties of the atom, as the following information about the electron theory shows.

The smallest and lightest atom is hydrogen, a gas which combines with oxygen in minerals that yield water when heated. Hydrogen (as suggested in Fig. 4) has one proton in its nucleus and one electron circling outside; hence its atomic number is 1. The next element is helium, a noninflammable gas used in balloons and dirigibles; its atom has two protons and two electrons, hence its atomic number is 2 (see Fig. 4). As the number of electrons increases, so does

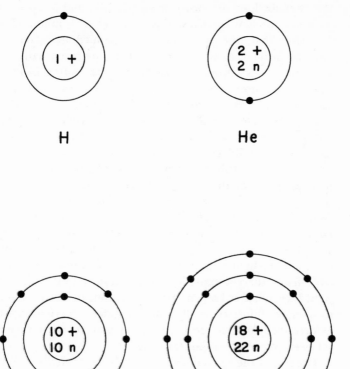

H          He

Ne

A

Fɪɢ. 4—Sketches of hydrogen, helium, neon, and argon atoms. Electrons encircle the nucleus which consists of positively charged protons and neutral neutrons.

the atomic number; however, only a few electrons can go in each concentric ring or shell, and then additional shells are needed. Two electrons are enough to complete the innermost shell, as already indicated for helium, 8 more fill the next shell, ending with neon (Fig. 4), and 8 more are sufficient to close the third shell, ending with argon (Fig. 4). After that, the outer shell is expanded to accommodate additional electrons; new shells are eventually required, the next two (of 8 electrons each) ending in krypton and xenon, respectively. The final shell is also concluded with 8 electrons, becoming radon.

You will note that all the elements possessing complete shells of electrons are inert, which means that their atoms will not normally enter into chemical combination with other elements. Instead, they are found floating as independent gases in the earth's atmosphere and they can be separated from the rest of the air without chemical treatment. This rugged individualism of an element that will neither accept electrons from other elements nor give up any of its own ample supply is responsible for making helium safe for lighter-than-air craft, for it will not unite with oxygen and thereby explode. The use of neon in illuminated signs is even better known. Argon functions in electric bulbs to show the fluorescence of minerals under ultraviolet light, as described in Chapter 11. Krypton and xenon have not yet been put to any significant use.

The rest of the elements, having incomplete shells of electrons, are like unmarried persons looking for a mate. They will combine with elements of their own choosing to form compounds, which are then more or less stable because the electrons, previously held loosely, are now rightly shared by each element of the new compound. Fig. 5 shows this marriage of one atom of sodium (a light, silvery metal) and one atom of chlorine (a poisonous greenish yellow gas); the resulting compound is sodium chloride, which in solid form is the mineral halite, common table salt. The smallest amount of a compound that has all the chemical properties of that compound is called a molecule; in this instance one atom of both elements is required to build a molecule of sodium chloride—anything less would not give, for instance, a salty taste.

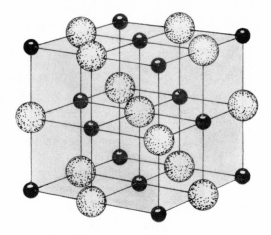

Fig. 5—Atomic structure of halite. Large ions are chlorine; small ions are sodium.

Inasmuch as the number of negatively charged electrons in an atom equals the number of positively charged protons, as already stated, atoms are electrically neutral. So are molecules and compounds. Nevertheless, most minerals are constructed, not of molecules of the compounds, but of an endless three-dimensional network of charged atomic particles called ions, which attract one another to form a stable compound. Table salt will again serve as an example. The sodium atom, losing its single outer electron to the newly formed compound, becomes positively charged. The chlorine atom gains the negative charge of the shared electron. Opposite charges attract each other and so the two ions unite as described.

These successive ions spread throughout the entire structure, which in a crystalline mineral (see page 107) is known as a crystal lattice. The smallest amount of a lattice having all the features of the whole mineral is called a unit cell. In halite the unit cell consists of 4 ions of sodium and 4 ions of chlorine, arranged as shown in Fig. 5. This unit cell is the structural equivalent of a chemical molecule, each being the smallest package necessary to carry all the respective properties of the substance.

Chemists use a convenient shorthand to express the composition of minerals and other substances. The names of the elements are abbreviated to one or two letters and then turned into symbols by omitting the period. All except ten of the abbreviations are those of the ordinary English name of the element, such as C for carbon, I for Iodine, and Pt for platinum. The rest are derived from the Latin name, such as K for *kalium,* potassium; Fe for *ferrum,* iron; and Au for *aurum,* gold. A complete list of the elements may be found in the larger dictionaries and in textbooks on chemistry. The eight most abundant elements in the rocks and minerals of the earth's crust are as follows: oxygen (O), silicon (Si), aluminum (Al), iron (Fe), calcium (Ca), sodium (Na), potassium (K), and magnesium (Mg).

The same shorthand is carried over from elements into compounds, where it expresses the chemical composition by means of a *formula.* The formula $NaCl$ for halite means that it contains one atom of sodium for each atom of chlorine. Pyrite has the formula $FeS_2$, indicating that one atom of iron is combined with two atoms of sulfur. A more complex formula is that of corundum, with two atoms of aluminum and three of oxygen, $Al_2O_3$. And then there is tourmaline: $(Na,Ca)(Mg,Al,Fe,Li)_3Al_6(BO_3)_3(Si_6O_{18})(OH)_4$. No wonder John Ruskin wrote of tourmaline, "The chemistry of it is more like a medieval doctor's prescription than the making of a respectable mineral!"

## CHEMICAL CLASSES OF MINERALS

The principal classifications of minerals, both scientific and industrial, are based primarily upon their chemistry. The simplest in composition are, of course, the minerals composed of only one *element.* These include the native metals, such as gold, iron, and silver; the nonmetals, such as sulfur, diamond, and graphite; and the semimetals such as arsenic, bismuth, and tellurium, which may act chemically either as metals or as nonmetals. Since the elements occurring naturally by themselves (therefore, as minerals) include iron, copper, and sulfur, but not calcium or phosphorus (which do not exist alone in nature), the term minerals as applied to certain constituents of food is used wrongly. Elements are what are really meant, although they are indeed derived from the minerals of the soil. An ever-increasing number of elements are found to be essential to life.

Graphite is one of the most interesting minerals occurring as a native element. In Ceylon it is found in rich vein-like concentrations, whereas in Madagascar it is scattered in irregular blobs throughout the rock. Its occurrence in New York near the Revolutionary War fort of Ticonderoga is indicated by the name of the Ticonderoga pencil, for graphite is the material used as the "lead" in lead pencils. Most crystals of graphite are roughly six-sided and some have triangular markings on their flat surfaces. Being elemental carbon, graphite is chemically the same as diamond, though the atomic structures of the two minerals are obviously very different, as proved by the tremendous unlikeness in their physical characteristics. Graphite is known to be the ultimate product resulting from the complete transformation of coal after all the volatiles have been driven off, leaving only "fixed" carbon. Most graphite, however, has not originated from coal but as natural deposits modified by temperature and pressure in the usual fashion of ordinary rocks and minerals.

The crystals of sulfur from Sicily are remarkably large and well shaped. Volcanic activity is generally responsible for the formation of this native mineral, which deposits about the orifices of natural vents that give forth sulfurous gases, as at Pozzuoli near Naples; around hot mineral springs and geysers, as in Iceland; and around the craters of volcanoes, as on the island of Vulcano in the Mediterranean Sea. An odd occurrence of finely crystallized sulfur is in beds of asphalt at Perticara, Italy. Sulfur is common in the volcanic regions of the world, which are distributed prominently in four great zones stretching across the earth. These include the broad "circle of fire" bordering the Pacific Ocean; another band that follows the Mediterranean and appears again in the Hawaiian Islands; a belt extending down the mid-Atlantic southward from Spitzbergen; and a parallel zone reaching from Palestine to Madagascar.

Native platinum is a rare mineral and nuggets of it are highly desired, both commercially and as specimens. A record 21-pound piece was picked up on the western coast of South America in 1897. When first noticed by Europeans about 1735 in stream gravels in the Rio Pinto in Colombia, it was named platina del Pinto ("silver of the Pinto") from its resemblance to silver. With the price of platinum now about three times that of gold, it is amusing to recall that counterfeit coins were once made by plating disks of platinum with a thin covering of gold. The two metals weigh about the same and the deception was not readily detected. Later, platinum was used openly for coinage in Russia until its value exceeded that of the money. Today, besides its familiar use in jewelry, platinum has strategic military uses in the electrical and chemical industries. Natural platinum is unknown without most of the other metals of the so-called platinum group being present; these are palladium, iridium, osmium, rhodium, and ruthenium. Platinum and palladium are much more abundant than the other four members of this group. Either iridium or osmium—it has not yet been determined which—ranks as the heaviest of all metals.

*Sulfides* are the chemical class most typical of the ore minerals described in Chapter 13. In these minerals sulfur combines with a metal, such as with silver to form argentite, but occasionally it unites with a semimetal, as with antimony to form stibnite. When sulfur is combined with both a metal and a semimetal, the mineral is regarded as a *sulfosalt;* an example is stephanite, a sulfide of silver and antimony, which was one of the main silver ores in the Comstock Lode, near Virginia City, Nevada. Oxygen is absent from all such minerals. The sulfides range from black to silver white, showing green, red, blue, and other colors, and the luster of most of them is recognizably metallic.

Realgar and orpiment are two nonmetallic sulfide minerals of especial attractiveness. They occur together in bright masses of red and yellow. Exposure to light causes the red or orange realgar to alter in time to the yellow orpiment. Both are sulfides of arsenic, occurring in regions of hot springs, including Norris Geyser Basin in Yellowstone National Park. They were formerly used in fireworks, pigments, and other chemical preparations but have now been replaced by artificial compounds having the same composition.

Stibnite, a sulfide of antimony, is one of the best crystallized of minerals. A series of tiny movements called gliding frequently gives crystals of stibnite the appearance of being curved or bent. The magnificent clusters of shiny gray stibnite crystals once numerous on the island of Shikoku, Japan, are seen in museums throughout the world. Few minerals are more in demand by collectors than these splendid specimens.

Another sulfide mineral, one that should be better known, is millerite, a nickel sulfide usually growing in delicate hairlike or needle crystals. It has a brassy or bronzy color. Milwaukee, Wisconsin, is one of the localities where this mineral is found in hollow rocks called geodes (see page 39), in which tangled tuffs of millerite penetrate calcite crystals. Back in 1789 the geologist Werner called these yellow wires Haarkies.

The ease with which oxygen unites with other elements makes possible the large and important class of minerals called *oxides*. Some of them are ores of metals, including iron, copper, zinc, and tin. Some are gems, such as corundum, spinel, and chrysoberyl. A few are minor rock-making minerals, including rutile and chromite. And, of course, ice is an oxide of hydrogen. The oxides can be divided into

Fɪɢ. 6—Japanese stibnite crystals from Ichinokawa, Iyo province, Shikoku island, are the world's choicest. (*Courtesy of Ward's Natural Science Establishment.*)

several groups—simple oxides, which are compounds of one metallic element and oxygen; multiple oxides, containing two metals and oxygen; hydroxides, which give up water when heated; and special oxides set aside as warranting separate consideration. One mineral of each of these kinds is described below.

Litharge is a curious lead mineral found in the oxidized zones of lead deposits. It was once thought to exist almost entirely as an artificial product, supposed to have originally been obtained during the metallurgical process of extracting silver from lead. Litharge is now believed to be fairly common in at least a few places in California and perhaps in lead mines elsewhere. Although colored red it should not be confused with minium, the true "red lead," which is also an oxide of the same metal.

The *multiple oxides* are represented by hausmannite, which was discovered as a coating on other minerals in cavities left by gas escaping from the rock. Sweden and Brazil are known for fine crystals of hausmannite.

Brucite is one of the *hydroxides*. This pearly white magnesium mineral consists of flexible plates, somewhat resembling mica, somewhat resembling talc or gypsum. Well-developed crystals come from Texas in Pennsylvania, Brewster in New York, and Asbestos in Quebec.

Among the special groups of oxides are those containing radioactive elements, such as uranium and thorium, and certain metals, such as titanium and niobium. Apart from the radioactive minerals, which are described in Chapter 10, probably the most important of these oxides is columbite, which grades completely into tantalite. A flattened group of columbite crystals taken from the Ingersoll mine near Keystone, South Dakota, weighed nearly a ton. Columbite is a black mineral associated with the coarse rock called pegmatite (see Chapter 9), in which it is widely distributed in the United States and other countries.

The *halides* are a chemical class containing compounds of the four halogen elements—chlorine, fluorine, bromine, and iodine. By far the most dominant of such compounds is sodium chloride, the mineral name for which is halite (see page 110).

Next in abundance is fluorite, also known as fluorspar. This handsome calcium fluoride mineral comes in almost every color; its sharp cubes often reveal zones of different hues side by side, and the original colors may be modified by heat, pressure, X-rays, and ultraviolet light—which gives rise to the fluorescence described in Chapter 11. Fluorite is associated with many ore deposits. The English crystals are unsurpassed for beauty and perfection. In the United States the large sea-green cubes from New York, the purple ones from Illinois and Kentucky, and the yellow ones from Ohio are choice enough for any collection.

Another halide mineral, carnallite, is a source of potash compounds used as fertilizers. It is a white mineral recovered in granular masses from the famous salt beds of Stassfurt in Germany, where the only complete sequence of ocean salts is known ever to have accumulated. Carnallite is found elsewhere, but mainly in the Stassfurt area.

*Carbonates* are compounds of carbon, oxygen, and at least one additional element. They are readily identified by the hissing and fizzing (called effervescence) which results when they dissolve in acid. This sound is due to the escape of carbon dioxide gas from the mineral. Sometimes a drop of cold weak acid such as vinegar will produce vigorous action, as with calcite, but some carbonates need a warm and stronger acid.

Some of the carbonates are extraordinarily significant minerals. Leading the others in abundance is calcite, calcium carbonate, which is the essential constituent of limestone and most marble. Substituting for calcite in some marble is dolomite, which is a calcium-magnesium carbonate. The pure magnesium carbonate, at the other end of this series, is magnesite. Siderite, the iron carbonate; rhodochrosite, the manganese carbonate; and smithsonite, the zinc carbonate, also belong to this so-called calcite group.

Calcium carbonate likewise occurs in a different mineral form known as aragonite. Related to it are a barium carbonate, witherite; a strontium carbonate, strontianite; and a lead carbonate, cerussite. This last one requires nitric acid if it is to give more than a short spurt of hissing.

Whereas sulfides are composed of sulfur in combination with other elements but not oxygen, a different class of minerals, called *sulfates*, consists of sulfur and oxygen together with other elements. Thus the common lead sulfide, galena, takes up oxygen upon weathering and becomes lead sulfate, which is known as anglesite because of its discovery on the island of Anglesey, in the Irish Sea off the coast of Wales.

Barite is one of the major sulfate minerals. Clear blue crystals of characteristic shape are picked out of clay in two Colorado localities—near the small towns of Stoneham and Hartsel. Crystals of spectacular beauty come from England. Owing to its weight, inertness, and stability, common barite is employed in many industries, making, for example, the chief component of interior paint, the shiny surface of playing cards, and a heavy "mud" for drilling oil wells.

Epsomite, the original Epsom salts from Epsom, England, is a hydrous magnesium sulfate. It is typical of many such compounds that deposit on the walls of mines and the roofs of caves. Snowballs of epsomite adhere to the ceiling of Mammoth Cave in Kentucky. Its curled fibers are suspended from the tunnels inside numerous Western mines and drop onto the miners as they work, the astringency giving a brief sensation of sharpness against the skin.

Phosphorus unites with oxygen to produce, in combination with other elements, the *phosphate* minerals. Apatite is one of the best-known of these. Its main occurrence is in small grains in igneous rocks, and in phosphate rock as the variety collophanite. Large six-sided crystals of apatite are at home in pegmatites and in metamorphic rocks, as is true of the huge crystals in the ancient rocks of Ontario and Quebec. Besides the usual brown and green shades, apatite may have other colors; in fact, so much does it look like several other minerals that it received its name from a Greek word meaning "to deceive."

Amblygonite is a phosphate occurring in large, coarsely crystalline masses. It contains lithium, useful in many ways in modern industry. Amblygonite rather closely resembles spodumene, another lithium mineral, both being characterized by the blunt or right-angled edge with which they may break. These minerals, plus petalite and lepidolite, have had close competition from the brines of Searles Lake, in the Mojave Desert of California, which is also a major supplier of potash, borax, and several sodium compounds.

Pyromorphite, another phosphate mineral, is remarkable for its hollow crystals which so often resemble the battlements of an old castle. It is a heavy mineral and has a resinous green surface. Many European localities furnish good specimens.

FIG. 7—Structure of silicate tetrahedron.

Substituting arsenic or vanadium for phosphorus in the phosphates gives us the *arsenates* and *vanadates,* which are among the most brilliantly colored of all minerals. Two of these, mimetite and vanadinite, have the same crystallization as pyromorphite, described above. Wonderful deep-red crystals of vanadinite from Arizona are treasured in leading museums.

The most numerous, as well as the most complex, of the inorganic chemical compounds in nature are the *silicates.* The fundamental structure is a combination of silicon and oxygen in the tetrahedral pattern shown in Fig. 7, whereby one silicon atom in the middle is surrounded by three oxygen atoms at the corners. These tetrahedrons unite with one another and with additional elements in such a way as to build up the large number of silicate minerals, which can be counted in the hundreds. Aluminum has an especial tendency to substitute for silicon in the silicate framework, so that there are more aluminum silicate minerals than any other kind.

A zone some ten miles thick of the outer layer of the earth's crust has been studied carefully by geologists and chemists. Their work has been done largely by sampling and estimation, for even this relatively thin zone extends fully two and one-half times as far down from the surface as the deepest hole in existence, the 25,340-foot Texas oil well. Henry S. Washington and Frank W. Clarke calculated that 95 per cent of this ten-mile zone consists of igneous ("fire") rocks (including metamorphic [modified] rocks that had previously been igneous), of which feldspar makes up 59.5 per cent, pyroxene and amphibole 16.8 per cent, quartz 12.0 per cent, mica 3.8 per cent, and "minor minerals" a total of 7.9 per cent. The minerals named here are all silicates, and most of the undifferentiated minor minerals are likewise silicates. These figures indicate vividly the outstanding importance of the silicate class as rock-forming minerals. (The chief minerals of igneous rocks are described in Chapter 5.)

## MINERAL RELATIONSHIPS

The chemical classes of minerals, as already described, are subdivided into *types* according to a decreasing ratio of positive to negative ions or electrostatically charged atoms—such as the metals and nonmetals among the native elements. Types are further divided into *groups,* which usually consist of minerals of closely similar structure, or sometimes of minerals having like chemical compositions or physical properties warranting their being described together—such as the gold group, which also embraces silver and copper. *Series* include minerals that show a continuous variation in properties with changing chemical composition, such as plagioclase feldspar. *Species* are independent minerals or else the major members of a series. *Varieties* are mostly chemical variations from the principal composition of a series, though many of the older varieties were named because of distinctive physical properties (such as ruby, a red corundum) or a special origin (such as travertine, a calcite of hot- or cold-spring birth).

# 5

# Origin of Rocks and Minerals

Little is known about the interior of the earth. In our daily lives we have contact with only a small part of the outer zone of the planet on which we live. This zone is called the crust, a reminder of the days when it was believed to be the hardened shell that had chilled on the surface of a globe still molten inside. The rest of the earth is hidden from view, and even much of the estimated 18 to 50 miles of the crust itself has not yet been exposed by erosion or penetrated by man-made holes.

Compared to the size of the earth, the thickness of the crust that has been revealed thus far is trivial, no more than the thickness of the top page in a five-foot shelf of books piled one upon another.

The deepest well that has been drilled for petroleum reached 25,340 feet in Pecos County, Texas, although the lowest actual production of oil has come from shallower depths.

A number of metal mines are nearly 9,000 feet deep. Some in the Kolar gold fields of India and the Witwatersrand gold district of South Africa come close to that figure. The deepest mine in the world is the Crown gold mine at Johannesburg, Republic of South Africa, which may be nearing 10,000 feet, and the deepest in North America is Shaft Number 4 of the Lake Shore mine at Kirkland Lake, Ontario, which has passed 7,750 feet.

Even the natural irregularities of the earth's surface are slight compared to its diameter. From North Pole to South Pole the earth measures 7,899.7 miles; through the equator it is 7,926.5 miles. Contrast these figures with 12.2 miles,

which is the difference between the top of the highest mountain, Mount Everest in the Himalayas, 29,028 feet above sea
level, and the greatest known depth in the ocean, 36,173 feet
below sea level, at a point located offshore in the Marianas
Trench near Guam, in the Pacific. Thus the earth is relatively as smooth as a billiard ball, and man has done no
more than make tiny pin pricks into its hard surface.

Having only this superficial acquaintance with our planet,
we require considerable ingenuity to deduce the conditions
that may exist deep inside it. The center of the earth, less
than 4,000 miles away, is as inaccessible as stars that are so
distant that light coming from them takes millions of years
to arrive here, but which can be seen through telescopes and
analyzed chemically by means of spectrometers and other
optical instruments.

Geologists and astronomers have worked on this problem
from many angles. They have measured the size of the earth
by the geodetic methods of spherical trigonometry. They
have weighed it by determining the gravitational attraction
between it and other celestial bodies. They have calculated
the speed and direction of earthquake waves, in order to
learn what sort of substances the hidden rocks consist of and
how they are distributed. By studying meteorites, which (as
explained in Chapter 12) may correspond to the material
that composes the core of the earth, they have hoped to find
out more about a part of the universe that will probably
never be available for direct study.

It was once thought that beneath its thin crust the earth
was a body of seething hot liquid. With growing evidence
that this molten condition was not likely, students of earth
science postulated instead a zone of liquid which on occasions escaped to the surface to become lava or erupted with
explosive violence to create a volcano. The study of earthquake or seismic waves has caused even this hypothesis to
be modified.

The earth transmits waves of three main kinds. One kind,
called longitudinal, compressional, or primary (P) waves,

travels between 4 and 8 miles per second, according to the elasticity and density of the material through which they pass. Another kind, called transverse or secondary (S) waves, travels between 2.5 and 4.2 miles per second, reaching the recording station after the other. These are both known as preliminary waves or body waves, because they arrive early after moving in all directions through the interior of the earth. Because the transverse waves do not pass through liquids, yet manage to travel along various paths through the outer 55 per cent of the entire earth, it is inferred that at least this outer shell is essentially solid. The third main kind of seismic wave is the long or surface wave, which goes relatively slowly around the earth rather than across it. Each of these types of waves gives rise to a number of varieties when it strikes a boundary between two zones of different rock. The condition of the core is not fully understood, but it is thought that it must be much heavier than the known rocks at the surface (see page 167) and that it is under enormous pressure. The latest research indicates that the core may be regarded as being composed of solid iron surrounded by molten iron, made turbulent by jet streams and swirling currents like those of the upper atmosphere.

In spite of the apparent solidity of the outer part of the earth, molten rock, water and other liquids, and steam and other gases are seen to issue from beneath the surface and must come from some source at present unknown. It seems probable that, even if no zone of molten rock entirely encircles the earth at some definite depth, pockets of such material are localized in certain places. Or, if not actually molten, these small bodies of rock may be potentially liquid but kept in a semiplastic state by the pressure of the overlying solid rock.

When this pocket of rock melts—as a result of overheating by radioactivity, combined with reduced pressure as fissures open above it—it wells up, forcing or eating its way toward the surface as *magma,* which is a mixture of melted rock and dissolved gases. Magma loses most of its gas upon reaching the surface, where it becomes *lava*.

## IGNEOUS ROCKS AND MINERALS

As magma or lava cools and solidifies or crystallizes, it forms igneous rocks, the first of the three main types of rock. The others are the sedimentary and metamorphic rocks, to be described later.

**Igneous Rocks.** As the word igneous (related to ignite) suggests, these are the fire-made rocks. With them are associated all the varied phenomena of vulcanism, which includes the internal activities of magma as well as the external features of lava and true volcanoes, though the term is often preferred for the surface effects alone. Igneous rocks that have solidified beneath the surface, from magma, are called *intrusive rocks;* those that have solidified upon the surface, from lava or volcanic fragments, are referred to as *extrusive rocks.*

The rocks of each of these types reveal their history by their appearance. Intrusive rocks, losing heat slowly during their long confinement within the earth, develop a coarse texture as the individual mineral grains have an opportunity to grow out of the magma to appreciable size. The fluids that are present lower the temperature of crystallization, thus keeping some of these rocks molten for a longer time than would otherwise elapse. Granite, showing crystals of several minerals visible to the unaided eye, is the most common example of such an intrusive rock. Other important intrusive rocks are gabbro and diorite.

The loss of gas as magma turns into lava, and the rapid cooling of lava exposed to the air, prevent large crystals from growing, and so the resulting texture is fine grained. Basalt, with a closely knit fabric of mineral grains which need a microscope to be identified, is a typical example of such an extrusive rock. The cooling may even take place so quickly that crystallization can scarcely begin, and a solid body of natural glass will be the chief product. Obsidian is glass formed in this way.

Besides the rate of cooling, other factors, including pressure and especially the chemical composition of the original magma, influence the kind of minerals that will form in an igneous rock, the size to which they will grow, and the pattern they will take.

GRANITE. The most extensively occurring igneous rock is granite. The "strength of granite" is a byword, for granite indeed has the strength of mountains. It constitutes the central core of many great mountain ranges, where it has been exposed by long-continued erosion through past ages. World-wide in distribution, granite is the typical bedrock of the continents and is associated with some of the most important ore deposits.

Two minerals, quartz and feldspar, are essential to granite, though others are usually present to some extent. The feldspar may be of two kinds, potash-soda feldspar or plagioclase, though sometimes only one of these is present. In addition are found mica (mostly biotite), hornblende, magnetite, and lesser minerals. Granite is referred to as a silicic igneous rock because it contains quartz, there having been enough silica present to crystallize out by itself.

As the feldspar varies from white to dark gray or even red, and the proportion of other minerals changes, many colors of granite are produced, lending themselves to numerous architectural uses. The red Pikes Peak granite is one of the attractive varieties, helping to give the rosy glow of sunrise for which this mountain is famous. A similar rock from St. Cloud, Minnesota, is frequently used in buildings. Quincy granite from Massachusetts and Barre granite from Vermont are well-known commercial varieties. Scottish granite is an outstanding choice for beauty and durability.

BASALT. Another prominent igneous rock is basalt. It is quite complementary to granite, for in origin it is an extrusive rock, having formed mostly in widespread lava flows, and its chemical composition is spoken of as basic, as it contains abundant iron and magnesium, which are relatively scarce elements in granite. Basalt is therefore a dark, heavy, and fine-grained rock. Its essential minerals are plagioclase feldspar (usually labradorite) and pyroxene (usually augite), but these and other minerals that may be present occur in grains that are usually too small to be recognized without magnification.

On several occasions during the Tertiary period of geologic history—the time immediately preceding the recent Ice Age—vast floods of lava poured forth from numerous cracks in the earth's crust, rolled over the existing landscape, and hardened into basalt. The Columbia Plateau is built of such a sequence of basaltic lava flows, which piled up to a height of 4,000-6,000 feet, originally covering more than 200,000 square miles of eastern Oregon and Washington and southern Idaho. Another, greater area of basalt in the Deccan Plateau of India measured 500,000 square miles and was as much as 10,000 feet thick. Remnants of a third region similarly blanketed by basalt reach from Iceland to Scotland and Ireland, though the waves of the Atlantic have plucked away or inundated large parts of the original flow, once 10,000 feet in thickness. Modern flows of basalt in Iceland are the grandest within historic times; in 1783, from the 20-mile-long fissure called the Skaptar Cleft, three cubic miles of lava spread 100 feet deep to places 40 miles distant.

Many modern volcanoes consist largely of basalt—Etna, for example, and the whole of the Hawaiian Islands. This rock is not, of course, confined to present or recent geologic time, for the processes of nature go on "with no sign of a beginning—no prospect of an end." When used for railroad ballast, road construction, and buildings, basalt is often called trap rock, a term especially familiar in northeastern and northwestern cities of the United States.

OBSIDIAN, a natural glass. Obsidian Cliff in Yellowstone National Park is the nearest acquaintance that most Americans have with the hills of natural glass that dot the West

Fig. 8—Typical occurrence of basalt is this dramatic lava flow and cleft in Ódádahraun, central Iceland. (*Photo by Pall Jonsson, courtesy of Legation of Iceland.*)

and are a familiar sight elsewhere in regions marked by volcanic activity. This material is called obsidian after someone named Obsidius, who was supposed to have first found it in Ethiopia, though the story is a poor sort of legend.

Owing to its compact and uniform structure, obsidian could be chipped and flaked into pointed and sharp-edged objects used by primitive man for weapons and implements. The art of spalling off blades of obsidian six inches or more in length was highly developed by the ancient inhabitants of Mexico. The American Indians of every tribe worked up arrowheads, spearpoints, and knives in enormous quantities. Even earlier, the bright surface of obsidian was used for mirrors in various parts of the world.

Most obsidian is as black as jet, but occasionally some is found in gray, brown, and red colors, often mixed together in a marble pattern. When broken into thin pieces, however, obsidian is found to be almost entirely clear, except for a fine sprinkling of dusty grains of magnetite that had barely started to crystallize. This mineral traps the light and renders the glass black; when oxidized to hematite, it results in obsidian having a red or brown color.

Chemical analyses of obsidian show it to have the same composition as an average granite. Only extremely rapid cooling prevented the growth of quartz, feldspar, and other constituents of typical granite. Instead, the result is a glass that is often difficult to tell from the product of a glass factory.

KIMBERLITE, mother of diamonds. One of the most interesting of the basic igneous rocks is kimberlite. It is the only original home of diamond, the most remarkable of minerals and the king of gems. Kimberlite is, like granite, an intrusive rock, having formed deep within the earth and then been exposed by erosion, but its chemical composition is basic, like basalt. Subsurface and atmospheric weathering have changed the fresh rock, known as peridotite, into its present broken and altered condition. The most abundant minerals are olivine and two members of the pyroxene group (bronzite and chrome-diopside); the most important mineral is of course diamond.

Named after the diamond city of Kimberley, this is the rock that occupies the cylindrical bodies called diamond pipes. Prior to their discovery here in 1870, the world's supply of diamonds had always come from secondary sources in sedimentary rocks, which had yielded all the famed Indian and Brazilian stones. The primary volcano or pipe deposits of kimberlite, though relatively restricted in distribution, occur in clusters throughout the southern half of the African continent. They range from 50 feet to half a mile in diameter. Most are entirely barren, and even the richest pipe contains diamonds only sparsely—the most pro-

Fig. 9—Forty-carat diamond crystal attached to kimberlite, the mother rock in the diamond pipes of South Africa. (*Courtesy of De Beers Consolidated Mines, Ltd.*)

ductive of all yielded at depth barely one part of diamond to 8 million parts of rock. Only large-scale mining at low cost could make such deposits profitable.

The top layer of kimberlite in the diamond mines is called "yellow ground" because of the color produced by oxidation. Beneath it is the "blue ground," which is likewise weathered; both layers disintegrate upon exposure to the air and set free their gemmy treasure.

It may seem strange to find kimberlite in America, but it is not unknown here, and a diamond pipe, very similar to those around Kimberley, has been worked at intervals since 1906 in Pike County, Arkansas. Attempts to exploit it commercially have repeatedly failed. The largest crystal found, however, weighed 40 carats and was of good quality.

PORPHYRY. The term porphyry belongs to the everyday language of Rocky Mountain prospectors and miners, who have long used it to refer to almost any hard rock associated with ore deposits. Properly, however, a porphyry is an igneous rock, whatever its occurrence, that contains crystals embedded in a finer-grained background, "like plums in a pudding." The crystals are known as phenocrysts and the rest is called the groundmass. A contrast in size between them is the only requirement for a porphyry; the groundmass may be glassy or quite coarse while the crystals are small or large—as long as there is any obvious difference in texture between them.

The original porphyry was a rock called *porfido rosso antico,* which occurred at Djebel-Dokhan in Egypt and was widely used as a building and ornamental stone because of the attractive appearance of its prominent crystals in a red or purple groundmass. Some porphyries are a prolific source of well-shaped crystals of feldspar and other minerals.

The significance of a porphyry is uncertain; some specimens suggest a sudden change in conditions after the early crystals had formed, whereas others indicate an excess of one sort of chemical compound which went into the making of the larger minerals.

**Igneous Minerals.** A relatively few minerals make up the bulk of the igneous rocks. The most abundant of these belong to one group known as the feldspars.

FELDSPAR. Orthoclase and microcline are spoken of as potash-soda feldspars because they contain potassium (potash) and sodium (soda), in addition to the aluminum, silicon, and oxygen present in all feldspars. The soda-lime feldspars, so called because of the presence of sodium and calcium (lime), form plagioclase, which is arbitrarily divided into six members for convenience. They look alike and usually need to be identified by chemical or microscopic means; labradorite alone has any characteristic appearance, often having a dark color.

Feldspar tends to be tabular in shape and shows a prominent cleavage surface; the plagioclase series may also show a fine grating of parallel lines due to multiple twinning of the crystals. Adularia is a pure variety of orthoclase with very little sodium, and is formed at low temperatures. Pretty pieces having an opalescent sheen are called moonstone. Sanidine is a glassy kind of high-temperature orthoclase found mostly in volcanic rocks. Green microcline is a gem stone familiarly known as amazonstone because it was supposed to occur near the Amazon River.

FELDSPATHOID. An interesting but rather scarce group of rock-making minerals are the feldspathoids. This name indicates the fact that they substitute for true feldspar when there is a deficiency of silica in the magma. Nepheline is a gray feldspathoid mineral with a greasy luster; it displays six-sided or rounded outlines. Leucite grows as white crystals shaped exactly like garnet. Sodalite is another feldspathoid, commonly white or gray, but sometimes it is a rich lavender-blue color. Noselite and hauynite are two other blue feldspathoids.

QUARTZ. No mineral is more widespread than quartz. In igneous rocks it can be recognized as a glassy colorless or gray mineral having no particular crystal shape because it formed late and filled the irregular spaces between the earlier grains. The handsome hexagonal crystals of quartz that adorn most mineral cabinets are found only in cavities or caves, not closely in the midst of other minerals as these normally exist in igneous rocks. Some of the more valuable varieties of quartz are described, together with other interesting gems, in Chapter 8.

MICA. Specimens of the mica group of minerals are remarkable for their perfectly elastic sheets. These can be bent sharply and, provided they are not broken, they will snap back to their original position. The individual flakes can be peeled apart until they are too thin to be handled. Other properties of mica are described in Chapter 16. Three main series of mica minerals are characteristic of igneous rocks. The most abundant by far is biotite, also known as black mica on account of its dark color; a related mineral with a smaller iron content is brown mica, called phlogopite. Muscovite, or white mica, often occurs in fine flakes referred to as sericite, which looks like artificial Christmas-tree snow. The lithium-bearing pink mica, lepidolite, is virtually confined to the remarkably coarse-grained rock, pegmatite, to which Chapter 9 is devoted.

PYROXENE. In 1796 Haüy gave the name pyroxene to a mineral which he regarded as a "stranger in the domain of fire," coining the word from two Greek words meaning "fire" and "stranger." The particular mineral was augite from the lavas of Mount Vesuvius, but Haüy believed it to have been accidentally trapped by the molten matter. Actually, pyroxene is a group of minerals that are, next to the feldspars, the most universal constituents of igneous rocks. They are, moreover, especially typical of rocks formed at the highest temperatures. Some of the recognized members of this group go under such names as enstatite, hypersthene, diopside, and, most commonly, augite. They are generally dark green or brown.

AMPHIBOLE. Another series of minerals, paralleling the pyroxenes in many respects, are the amphiboles. These usually form at lower temperatures and in the presence of fluids

Fig. 10—Crystals of mica are called books. Lepidolite seldom occurs in books as large as this one from the Brown Derby mine, Gunnison County, Colorado. (*Courtesy of Foote Mineral Co.*)

in the cooling rock. The major kind of amphibole in igneous rocks is hornblende, a mineral having an extremely complex chemical formula.

OLIVINE. Olivine crystallizes in igneous rocks at an early stage, when the molten magma is still very hot. This glassy-looking mineral gets its name from its olive-green color. It often occurs in small sugary grains which are easy to recognize. Some clear varieties are used as gems; peridot is the jeweler's name for a dark olive-green stone of pleasing though somewhat somber appearance. Olivine is an important mineral in meteorites (page 170). Large masses of it make up whole mountains in several parts of the world, as in New Zealand, where Dun Mountain gave its name to dunite, a rock composed almost exclusively of olivine.

ZEOLITE. Whereas the minerals described above are best developed in intrusive rocks, where they have an opportunity of growing to considerable size, the zeolites are most at home in the extrusive igneous rocks. This is particularly true of the heavy, dark rocks such as basalt, in which these minerals fill cavities caused by gas escaping from the molten lava as it spills across the land. The name zeolite, which means boiling stone, refers to the tendency of these minerals to bubble when heated, giving off water continuously. Furthermore, when exposed to water vapor—or even to such things as alcohol, iodine, and ammonia—the heated zeolites readily take them up. Among the important zeolites are analcime, resembling leucite and white garnet; stilbite, forming aggregates that resemble sheaves of grain; natrolite and thomsonite, each making clusters of delicate needles; chabazite, occurring in crystals that are nearly cubes; and heulandite, displaying diamond-shaped crystals.

## SEDIMENTARY ROCKS—THE BROKEN AND DISSOLVED ROCKS

The most deeply buried igneous rock will someday be uncovered by the processes of erosion. Then agents of chemical and mechanical weathering will cause it to decay and disintegrate. The weathered particles will be carried by water, wind, or glaciers and deposited elsewhere in layers, one upon another like pages in a book—the record in stone of our changing earth. Water is by far the most important factor in transporting this material, called sediment, although some of it is moved by wind, as sand is in dunes, and some is transferred by glacial ice. Water-borne sediment may settle out of the water simply on account of its weight, or it may be precipitated chemically from a state of solution. When converted into firm rock it constitutes the second major class of rocks, the sedimentary rocks. These are of a secondary nature, having been derived from earlier rocks, which may have been igneous in origin, or sedimentary (of a previous cycle) or metamorphic (the third class of rocks, which are discussed later).

Individual grains of sand, for example, may accumulate as sediment until they are changed into sandstone. Coarser pieces called gravel will make a conglomerate. Finer particles, clay or mud, will become shale. These are spoken of as clastic or detrital rocks, being composed of separate fragments of still-older rocks. They are named according to the kind or size of material in them. Arbitrary limits are set nowadays by geologists in order to secure greater precision in terminology, but the names are mostly common ones familiar to everyone.

The rock waste or sediment may have been gathered from an extensive area, or it may have come from a limited source. Many geologists have as one of their most important tasks the unraveling of the history of a given part of the earth by tracing the minerals in the sedimentary rocks of that locality back to their place of origin. Countless bits of seemingly unrelated evidence go into this scientific detective work. Professor W. H. Twenhofel of the University of Wisconsin, for instance, studied the size, rounding, and sorting of the grains in specimens of Pottsville sandstone collected from the top of Natural Bridge, Kentucky, and determined the rock to have been formed in an old stream channel.

Placers are sedimentary deposits of this kind that contain heavy and often valuable minerals, including gems and precious metals. So important are they that they deserve special attention in Chapter 13.

The other type of sedimentary rock consists of dissolved matter that has precipitated out of solution, either in some such manner as salt is deposited when a pan of salty water is evaporated, or by the action of certain plants and animals. During the erosion of the land by streams, an estimated 2,735,000,000 tons of rock is actually dissolved by the water and carried into the ocean annually. This colossal amount is sufficient to lower the entire land surface of the earth one foot in 30,000 years. In addition, a very small amount of material is dissolved along the coast by the washing of the waves, some is added directly by submarine and shore volcanoes, and some seeps into the ocean by means of underground water.

It is probable that the primeval ocean was entirely fresh water derived from the violent condensation of an extremely dense atmosphere. Although the old fairy tale gives a delightful explanation for "Why the sea is salt," the enormous amount of salt in the oceans today—calculated at 38,697,000,000,000,000 tons, enough to form a layer more than a mile and a half thick over the United States—must have been contributed during long ages by streams, ground water, volcanoes, and wave action. Hence the ocean is getting saltier all the time as it gathers more mineral matter from the land. Many mineral salts are present in marine water, but three-quarters of the solid content of average sea water consists of common salt, known chemically as sodium chloride and in mineralogy as halite. Some other compounds, especially calcium carbonate, calcium sulfate, and silica are actually being added to the ocean more abundantly than sodium chloride, but they are also being removed faster, whereas the sodium chloride is more soluble and stays in solution, neither depositing out nor being taken up by organisms. The kind of material carried down to the sea depends upon the kind of rock through which the streams travel. Rivers that flow from Canada into the North Pacific test mostly for calcium carbonate because they go through large areas of limestone, which has that composition. Farther south, rivers that cross the southwestern part of the United States bring more calcium sulphate because they move through a vast region of gypsum and anhydrite.

Sediments of either the clastic or chemical type become solid rock again by the process of *consolidation* or *lithification.* This includes *compaction,* whereby water is squeezed out and the individual particles are pressed together by the weight of the overlying sediments. It also includes *cementation,* whereby mineral matter is deposited between the grains to serve as a binder; almost any substance can act as a cement, but calcium carbonate, silica, and iron oxide are the most frequent. Also involved is *recrystallization,* which enables small particles to grow into large ones, or new minerals to form in the open spaces between other minerals.

In contrast to most igneous rocks—which are often spoken

of as massive because, having cooled from a molten state, they look much the same in all positions—sedimentary rocks generally have a marked parallel structure called *stratification*. Each layer or bed is laid down upon those already deposited, and there is a frequent change in color, texture, or minerals as one layer is added to another. If a layer is no longer horizontal, the natural inference is that it has been bent out of position since it was first deposited. When uniform conditions prevail over a long period, as they often do in the open ocean, the sediments may fail to show stratification except on a coarse scale. On the other hand, certain igneous rocks may show it well, as successive flows of different lava pile up on one another. Stratification is, nevertheless, the most distinctive feature of sedimentary rocks.

Sedimentary rocks also frequently contain *concretions,* which are nodules of mineral matter enclosed within other sediments. They occur in a wide range of sizes, shapes, and colors. Hollow nodules are called *geodes;* when lined with agate or various crystals they are eagerly sought by mineral collectors, each specimen furnishing a surprise when it is broken open to reveal bands of colorful agate or small bright crystals nestling among larger ones. The countless geodes that have been picked up by amateur mineral collectors in the vicinity of Keokuk, Iowa, are prized for their variety.

Marks left on the surface of sediments by water and the atmosphere are often preserved in the consolidated rock. Among these impressions are ripple marks made by the wind as it blows across sand dunes and by currents and waves as they lap upon the beach. Craterlets are made by raindrops during wet weather, and mud cracks result from the shrinkage of the ground in dry weather.

*Fossils* are confined almost exclusively to sedimentary rocks. The plants or animals that lived where the particular sediments were accumulating denote the nature of their environment. The presence of reef-building coral makes apparent the former existence of a warm, clear sea in that region. Figs in Greenland, coal swamps in the Antarctic, crocodiles in Minnesota, the tsetse fly in Colorado—these are a few of the other instances in which fossils give meaning to geology. Some fossils may have washed in from elsewhere and been incorporated in the new rocks; they then have little significance as to the environment, but at least they indicate how old the rocks are, according to the principle that organisms change with passing time, evolving into different and more highly developed forms of life. Thus, the oldest known horse, whose diminutive skeletons are found in sedimentary rocks of Eocene age, had four toes. Rocks of later times, situated at higher levels, show an increase in size and a decrease in the number of toes to the present single one of the modern horse, together with specialization in other ways that enabled the animal to adapt itself to changing habits and surroundings.

**Sandstone.** One of the most interesting and varied of the clastic sedimentary rocks is sandstone. The sand grains of which it is made are medium-sized fragments of older rocks and minerals. Typical sand consists of quartz, the commonest of the minerals that resist weathering and erosion and so gather readily wherever sediment accumulates. Some grains of quartz are rounded to perfection, though others are sharp-edged; some are smooth and shiny, while others are frosted by wind abrasion; some are sorted by nature as evenly as though they had been screened through a sieve, whereas others show a considerable range in size. If the particles fall within certain stated limits, however, they may still be regarded as sand. (The classification of sandstone is simplified in the table on page 100.)

Not all sand is composed of quartz. An entirely pure quartz sand, in fact, is a rarity. More likely feldspar, mica, garnet, magnetite, and other minerals are mixed with the quartz. A special type of sandstone is arkose, which contains a fairly large amount of feldspar. Much of the famous Old Red Sandstone of the British Isles is arkose, as is also

a good deal of the brownstone used in the so-called brownstone fronts, which were a mark of wealth in New York in
the middle of the nineteenth century.

Of even more interest are the sandstones made up of materials that we do not ordinarily think of as sand. The glistening heaps in White Sands National Monument near
Alamogordo, New Mexico, are drifting dunes of gypsum,
which in places have begun to stick together again to form
a solid rock. Countless tropical beaches are an expanse of
coral sand produced by the breaking up of reefs from the
incessant pounding of the waves. The Bay of Naples contains olivine sands of volcanic origin. Limestone sands are
found on the Swedish island of Gotland in the Baltic Sea,
in the St. Lawrence estuary, and in other places where the
cliffs are of limestone. Sand dunes on the coast of Galway
in Ireland are composed of pieces of coral and shell; a similar deposit in Bermuda has already consolidated into sandstone.

Black sands—given their dark color mostly by magnetite,
ilmenite, and chromite—are found in conspicuous streaks
where the selective action of waves and shore currents have
concentrated these heavy metallic minerals along the
beaches. The coasts of Oregon are especially noted for this
type of occurrence. Other black sands, like those along Lake
Superior, consist largely of pieces of volcanic rock from
eroded lava flows.

Yellow sands originate in the same way except that the
minerals are the heavy nonmetallic ones, such as zircon,
garnet, rutile, and monazite, which tend toward brown or
yellow colors. The extraordinary beach deposits of diamonds
in Namaqualand, along the Atlantic shore of South-West
Africa, where large quantities of diamonds have been found
associated with a certain kind of oyster shell, represent a
variety of heavy sand not to be expected frequently. Any
of these sands will become sandstone upon being cemented
together into firm rock. Thus, the diamond-bearing itacolumite of Brazil (described on page 219) is a flexible sand-

stone in which the gemmy crystals were added to the rest of
the minerals while the sand was being deposited.

**Conglomerate.** Gravel is the loose aggregation of material coarser in size than sand. It eventually becomes conglomerate when it turns to rock. Sand grains almost always
fill the spaces between the pebbles and boulders, the whole
assemblage being cemented together by percolating mineral-
laden water. Sometimes a distinction is made according to
the shape of the particles, those containing angular pieces,
with sharp edges and unworn corners, being referred to as
breccia.

Many conglomerates owe their origin to the ability of
glaciers to transport rock debris without sorting it by size,
as streams are obliged to do. Hence the roughest blocks and
boulders embedded in the ice advance at the same time as
the impalpably fine "rock flour" that the glacier has pulverized in its inexorable forward movement. As the ice melts,
the whole burden is dropped in an irregular pile known
by the Scottish name of till. The discovery of till among
other sedimentary rocks in various parts of the world provides evidence of former ice ages.

Conglomerates are prominent in the region of ancient
rocks extending from west of Lake Superior across southern
Canada to New England. The Great Conglomerate of northern Michigan and Wisconsin is 2,200 feet thick. Another
formation to which the same name was once applied lies
beneath the coal beds of Pennsylvania and adjacent states.
The Great Smoky Conglomerate is exposed in the Great
Smoky Mountains in North Carolina and Tennessee.

**Shale.** To a marked degree the most abundant sedimentary rock on all the continents is shale. It has formed by
the lithification of particles called mud, much finer than
sand and consisting mostly of the so-called clay minerals.
Like sand, mud can be composed of other things besides the
most typical material. Mica of several kinds is a common
constituent; quartz and other minerals are also generally
present in tiny grains. The clay and mica minerals are all

flaky ones, and they cause shale to split into thin layers with a characteristic shell-like surface.

Shale is much too weak to be used for building purposes, in contrast to so durable a rock as a hard sandstone. It does, however, slow up the settling of Portland cement and so is useful as a "retarder" in that essential structural material. A special type of shale, potentially valuable as a source of fuel, is the oil shale discussed in Chapter 15.

Most shale is of marine origin, having been deposited in the sea, the mud being carried out beyond the coarser particles which of necessity were dropped nearer the shore. Mud that accumulates in the open ocean far from land is augmented by wind-blown particles, as well as by those contributed by volcanoes, supplied by organisms, and rafted out by polar ice and floating aquatic plants. These sediments cover an enormous part of the globe and are known by such descriptive names as blue, gray, green, and black mud, and red clay. In one sample dredged from the central Pacific by the Challenger expedition, over 1,500 shark teeth and 50 ear bones of whales were counted. Shales of deep-sea origin are said to be present on Malta, Christmas Island, and the Barbados, and are believed to have been brought above sea-level by pronounced local upheavals.

**Coal.** Coal is an organic rock because it begins with the decay and burial of vegetation. It is considered a sedimentary rock because it is built up in layers by the gradual accumulation of the remains of generations of plants. Most coal has apparently been formed in coastal swamps, where lush plant life undergoes partial decomposition by bacteria and is covered by other sediments, which preserve it from complete destruction. The next step in the coal-making process is the formation of peat, and further transformation results in lignite or brown coal, then bituminous or soft coal, and, finally, anthracite or hard coal. Each change drives off more of the volatile substances as gases, leaving increasing concentrations of carbon, the real source of heat energy in these fuels. Elimination of everything except carbon yields graphite, though a good deal of graphite has also come about in other ways.

Every transition from the unaltered plants to the fossil leaves in graphite is known. Peat is commonly used as a home fuel in Ireland, and coal is being created in marshes and swamps today. The far-flung "Coal Measures," most bountifully supplied with this mineral wealth, belong to the interval of geologic time appropriately known as the Carboniferous period. Uniformly warm and humid climatic conditions prevailed then over broad areas of the earth, enabling a prolific plant growth to develop. Over 3,000 different species have been identified by their fossils. Incredible shrubs and rushes grew 100 feet high and ferns were as tall as trees.

Younger coal has generally not changed so thoroughly as coal in older deposits and so is commercially inferior. The colossal reserves of Wyoming and Colorado are of only moderate quality. The thickest bed of coal in the United States, measuring 84 feet, is at Adaville, Wyoming.

**Limestone.** Calcium carbonate comes out of solution to become limestone, chief among the sedimentary rocks that are formed in this way rather than by the settling of actual fragments, as happens with the clastic rocks sandstone and shale.

This mineral matter is converted into a deposit of limestone in two main ways. One is by saturation of the solution, whereby the excess calcium carbonate, which can no longer stay dissolved, is precipitated. Rising temperature, for example, will drive carbon dioxide gas out of the water, and this in turn reduces the amount of calcium bicarbonate that can remain dissolved. The surface of the warmer parts of the ocean is already well saturated with the substance, and little change is needed to cause some of it to settle out.

The other means by which limestone is produced consists of the action of plants and animals. These organisms remove calcium carbonate from the water in which they live and use it to strengthen their skeletons or to construct limey shells. Corals and the one-celled animals called foraminifera are among those especially responsible for the formation of large bodies of limestone throughout the world. The vital activities of some plants or animals cause calcium carbonate to precipitate, as when aquatic green plants extract carbon dioxide from the water. Thick layers of limestone have been made in this way by algae in Texas.

Pure limestone consists solely of grains of the mineral calcite. Being a carbonate, it fizzes briskly in acid, releasing carbon dioxide as a gas. Atoms of a related element, magnesium, often combine with those of calcium to form the mineral dolomite. Many limestones are dolomitic.

Limestone is one of the most important building stones. The quarry at Bedford, Indiana, yields an attractive fossil-bearing gray or tan stone that has found its way into churches, schools, and official buildings in every part of the United States, including most of the recently constructed large buildings in the national Capitol, such as the Pentagon. The Portland cement industry is based upon limestone as its most necessary raw material. Lithographic limestone, an extremely fine-grained variety, was formerly prized by artists and printers, but is now less frequently used.

Soils derived from limestone are noted for their fertility, as shown by the rich bluegrass region of Kentucky. Pulverized limestone is added to acid soils to offset their deficiency in lime.

Cave deposits of limestone are familiar as stalactites, which hang like icicles from the roof, and stalagmites, which build up like pillars from the floor. Hot and cold mineral springs deposit calcium carbonate as travertine, a porous rock which resembles Swiss cheese and is popular for decorative purposes in buildings. Mammoth Hot Springs in Yellowstone National Park is an immense occurrence of travertine. The agitation of the water in the Tivola River near Rome causes it to lose carbon dioxide and deposit travertine in the channel at a rapid rate. Travertine with colored bands is sold as Mexican onyx.

Chalk is another kind of limestone, which consists mostly of microscopic shells and plant remains that were deposited in warm, clear, shallow seas. The White Cliffs of Dover are striking beds of chalk formed in this way during the Cretaceous or chalk period of geologic history. The same rocks outcrop on the French side of the Channel.

**Gypsum.** When an enclosed body of sea water becomes separated from the ocean, or when a lake without an outlet evaporates in an arid climate, one of the most common salts to precipitate is hydrous calcium sulphate, known as gypsum. It is both a mineral and a rock. The mineral name for calcium sulphate without any water is anhydrite; it can change to gypsum in the presence of moisture, and the reverse change occurs when gypsum is heated or strongly compressed to force off the water.

Another common associate of gypsum is rock salt, because it originates in the same way, by the concentration of dissolved mineral matter until the water becomes saturated. The evaporation of a pile of sea water 770,000 feet high would be required to leave a bed of anhydrite 350 feet thick. This is so obviously unlikely that when we find marine deposits of nearly pure anhydrite thicker than that, as in western Texas, it is necessary to postulate some sort of a nearly land-locked basin, fed for a long time by repeated inflows of new water, each letting down a residue of calcium sulphate when it evaporated.

Compact gypsum is termed alabaster; tinted and mottled varieties from Colorado are carved into attractive ornamental and useful objects. Northern Italy is also an important source of compact gypsum. Switzerland and Sicily are sources of transparent gypsum, called selenite. Rock gypsum was employed to make plaster for the pyramids of Egypt, and it is today used in huge tonnages for plaster of Paris, so called because of the large deposits of gypsum underneath and surrounding the city of Paris. When three-fourths of the water in gypsum is boiled away, the resulting product is a quick-setting plaster.

## METAMORPHIC ROCKS AND MINERALS

Igneous and sedimentary rocks, when exposed to circumstances drastically different from those under which they originated, can change into metamorphic rocks, the third major type of rock.

Most minerals are, like living things, responsive to their environment. They are in general stable under the conditions existing at the time that they originated, but they become unstable in new surroundings. These are called diagnostic minerals because their presence in a rock suggests the sort of geologic environment from which the rock came. A few less-sensitive minerals, such as quartz and diamond, are able to maintain their identity during changed conditions. A small number of other minerals, such as native gold, are known as persistent minerals because they can be formed under many different conditions.

The cosmic state of affairs that existed when meteorites came into being is not known with certainty, but it must have been unlike the atmosphere we live in at the surface of the earth. Meteorites that hurtle through space and strike our planet, only to start crumbling into powder within a few years after they have been added to a museum collection, bear witness to this difference in environment.

Similarly, a piece of molten iron thrown from a blast furnace quickly succumbs to the oxygen and moisture in the air and rusts to hydrous iron oxide, which is more stable in the outside atmosphere.

Feldspar, the most abundant mineral in igneous rocks that are formed deep in the crust of the earth, readily weathers to clay at the surface. If this clay is later buried beneath a thick load of sediments, the increased pressure and temperature cause it to change into muscovite, garnet, and other metamorphic minerals which are more stable at depth. Such a transformation is called metamorphism. The term, however, does not include the simpler changes mentioned that are due to atmospheric weathering of a rock upon exposure to erosion, which must ultimately be the fate of all rocks, no matter how well hidden they now are.

Metamorphism is produced by heat, pressure, movement of the crust, and the chemical action of liquids and gases. Usually several of these factors are involved at the same time. The final result, which marks a metamorphic rock, is a significant change in texture or mineral composition, or both.

The most distinctive feature of metamorphic rocks is a layered or banded structure called foliation. It varies from thin slabs, as seen in slate used for roofing, to large lenses that give a crude streaked appearance to the rock. Foliation often resembles the bedding of sedimentary rocks, but it is due to the deformation of a pre-existing rock, which may be compressed, deformed, and sheared into patterns that range from closely parallel to wildly contorted. Foliation also resembles the flow structure of some igneous rocks, the minerals of which had been dragged out into layers while the cooling body of magma was becoming more viscous.

During the making of metamorphic rocks, the minerals in the earlier sedimentary or igneous rocks may undergo recrystallization, growing into larger crystals having a different orientation than before, or they may combine to form new minerals having a different chemical composition. Colored marble is an excellent example of both processes—the individual crystals of calcite in the original limestone recrystallize into coarser grains of calcite, and the impurities combine with one another and with the calcite to produce a new set of minerals.

**Contact Metamorphism.** As magma forces its way higher into the crust of the earth, there to cool and solidify as a body of intrusive igneous rock, the heat that is given off has a powerful effect upon certain of the surrounding rocks. Nor is this merely dry heat, for when minerals crystallize in the magma most of the enormous volume of liquids and gases that were originally dissolved in the molten mass are expelled from it, rising upward and outward into the adjacent rocks.

The combined action of the heat and fluids, the chief of which is water or steam, transforms the outer rocks. This is called contact metamorphism because it occurs at the place where the magma touches the rocks it has invaded. The actual transfer of material outward from the magma is particularly significant.

Some rocks, especially impure limestone and dolomite, will be profoundly changed, the foreign elements in carbonate rocks recombining to form an extensive list of new minerals typical of this sort of geologic occurrence. Most igneous and metamorphic rocks will be little altered, however, inasmuch as they have already been subjected to the energetic action of heat and fluids, and hence they are now too stable to be much bothered by this new event.

Mineral collectors acquire superior specimens of epidote, garnet, idocrase, and diopside among the minerals found in contact metamorphic zones. The addition of rare gases, such as fluorine and boron, furnishes the right ingredients to create various unusual minerals, including chondrodite and phlogopite mica. Ore deposits of some metals, especially wolfram (tungsten), have been formed by this same contact process.

**Metamorphic Rocks.** Because of their special qualities, the following section will describe briefly four major metamorphic rocks: slate, gneiss, marble, and quartzite.

SLATE. Intense pressure acting on shale, which is a sedimentary rock consisting largely of clay minerals (see page 201), changes it to slate by rotating the flaky grains until they lie with their flat surfaces facing the direction of the force. This direction, which rarely coincides with the original bedding, then marks the so-called slaty cleavage which enables the rock to split into the thin but broad slabs that are its chief feature.

The separate grains in slate are too small to be recognized without a microscope, but when magnified they are seen to be predominantly fine white mica (called sericite), chlorite (a flexible green mineral), quartz, and graphite or carbonaceous matter which provides the usual dark-gray color. Other pleasing colors in slate are green, purple, red, yellow, brown, and mottled tones.

Owing to its resistance to fire, its durability, and its strength, as well as its cleavage, slate is the main stone used in roofing. Being a nonconductor of electricity, slate functions well as material for switchboards. The slate blackboard is as authentic a symbol of schooldays as the school bell or flag.

Being a metamorphic rock, slate occurs in regions where ancient sediments were compressed into mountains. Pennsylvania, Vermont, Maine, and Georgia—all Appalachian states—are the leading producers. A slate mine, like the mines of other building stones, is called a quarry (see page 17). The rock is generally sawed by wires fed with abrasive. The broken blocks are then split by hand into suitable sizes.

GNEISS. At the other extreme from slate is the coarsest of the metamorphic rocks. It is spelled "gneiss" and pronounced "nīce," and is a nice source of puns for the beginner in geology until he settles down to serious business.

Gneiss may be derived from either an igneous or a metamorphic rock. The minerals in it are mostly feldspar, quartz, biotite and muscovite mica, and hornblende—the same as in an average granite. Whatever minerals were not originally present must have developed during the process of metamorphism. The grains are arranged in roughly parallel layers of alternating mineral content and appearance. As the layers lie closer and closer together, gneiss grades imperceptibly into another metamorphic rock, called schist. Occasionally the layers are so intricately twisted as to resemble the writhing of giant serpents.

Augen gneiss, named from the German word for eyes, encloses oval masses of feldspar or quartz set like huge eyes glaring from the rock. Other special kinds of gneiss indi-

cate the unusual minerals they contain. Thus we have garnet gneiss, a handsome rock sprinkled through with dark
red almandite garnets. Bundles of slender brown crystals of
sillimanite in some gneiss resemble embedded fibers of
brushes. Even the soft mineral graphite may occur in certain varieties.

MARBLE. Ranking unquestionably as the most beautiful
of all rocks, marble is prized for its inexhaustible variety.
The soft shimmering luster of close-grained marble gives
way to the lively sparkle of the more coarsely crystalline
kinds. In color, marble ranges from the snow-white purity
of classic statuary stone to the unrestrained swirls and vein-
ing so characteristic as to be known as marbling.

The sugary Carrara marble from Italy, the Parian marble
from the island of Paros, and the Pentelic marble from the
mainland of Greece, celebrated for the noble buildings and
works of sculpture created from them by the classic and
Renaissance masters, have their American equal in the
brilliant Yule marble of Colorado. The largest block was
used for the tomb of the Unknown Soldier in Arlington
National Cemetery, for which no piece of equal size (56
tons) could be found elsewhere in the United States. The
same marble was employed for the major part of the Lin-
coln Memorial in Washington; the 36 columns, 44 feet high
and 7 feet in diameter, are constructed of stone from this
locality in a remote wilderness area of the Rocky Mountains.

Pure marble such as this consists solely of recrystallized
grains of dolomite or calcite. These same minerals were
originally present in smaller crystals in a sedimentary carbonate rock, which was either dolomite or limestone (the
latter much more common), according to whether magnesium was present or not. In the trade, the name marble is
applied even to large blocks of limestone or dolomite if they
take a good polish, but correct usage restricts marble to
their metamorphic equivalents.

Striking patterns distinguish ornamental marble from

white statuary marble and uniformly colored architectural marble. The colors are due to the presence of impurities—clay, sand, and iron oxide, among others—in the earlier sedimentary rock. As metamorphism frees carbon dioxide gas from the calcium carbonate, the remaining lime combines with any nearby silica and other impurities to form numerous silicate minerals. Additional substances are also furnished during contact metamorphism, thus creating still more new minerals.

Bands and knots of these minerals produce striped, spotted, and cloudy marble of all kinds. A choice variety, with sinuous bands of green serpentine, is known as verde antique. When replaced by new minerals to an extreme degree, the carbonate rock turns into a silicate body defined by large amounts of such minerals as wollastonite, tremolite, diopside, and grossularite garnet.

Whether formed by contact metamorphism as previously described—whereby a heated or even molten igneous body moves upward into a zone of sedimentary rocks—or under conditions of great pressure—as during the crumpling that accompanies the making of a mountain range—marble lacks the foliation or layered structure so dominant in gneiss and schist. The reason is that calcite has a strong tendency to recrystallize rapidly, actually to flow plastically, while being transformed, and the bedded structure is destroyed in the doing.

QUARTZITE. Metamorphism of sandstone yields quartzite, a hard rock with a glistening appearance. The original quartz grains have been recrystallized in conjunction with the silica that cemented them together. Whereas a sandstone will break around the individual grains, the matrix of quartzite has become as coherent as the particles of quartz sand in it, and the rock shatters across both grains and matrix alike without regard to their original nature.

Quartzite can be told from marble, which may resemble it, by its failure to effervesce in acid and by being too hard to scratch with a knife. Like marble it is massive and does not show the foliation expected of most metamorphic rocks. No other rock is quite so durable as a good quartzite. Wherever it occurs to any extent, it supports hills and ridges, preserving them from erosion while the adjacent topography succumbs. Quartzite is widely distributed among the great mountain ranges of the world. The Nelson Range in British Columbia, for example, is also known as the Quartzite Range.

**Metamorphic Minerals.** Brief descriptions of some of the most important typically metamorphic minerals seem desirable here. In addition, certain minerals of igneous and sedimentary origin, already described in this chapter, would be recognized as essential components of many metamorphic rocks.

EPIDOTE. Epidote is a yellowish-green mineral, often of a peculiar shade referred to as pistachio green. In some places large masses of it occur, but its complex crystals are confined to cavities. Magnificent clusters of crystals have been taken from Prince of Wales Island, off the coast of Alaska, and choice epidote is also native to other countries.

IDOCRASE. Idocrase is the newly adopted name for vesuvianite, a mineral long known among the rocks altered by the eruption of Mount Vesuvius. Fine specimens are also found elsewhere in Italy. The shape of the crystals and their green and brown colors cause idocrase to resemble epidote and garnet.

DIOPSIDE. Diopside is a metamorphic member of the pyroxene group of minerals previously mentioned (page 73) as important constituents of high-temperature igneous rocks. Often a transparent pale green or white, diopside crystals are either scattered singly or bunched together and are especially common in marble. The Austrian Tyrol and the Italian Alps are noted sources of good specimens.

TREMOLITE. Rather similar to diopside but belonging instead to the amphibole group of minerals is tremolite. As the amount of iron increases, tremolite darkens, grading into green actinolite as it does so. The most familiar specimens of actinolite in the United States come from the huge talc quarry at Chester, Vermont.

ANDALUSITE, KYANITE, SILLIMANITE. Andalusite, kyanite, and sillimanite are three interesting minerals having exactly the same chemical composition, aluminum silicate. An odd variety of andalusite, known as chiastolite, contains inclusions of carbon distributed in a cross-shaped pattern that is visible when the ends of the square crystals are sliced and polished. Kyanite is an attractive blue and white mineral remarkable for its varying hardness in different directions, as described on page 31.

GARNET. Several kinds of garnet rank among the chief minerals in metamorphic rocks. These include almandite (the iron-aluminum garnet), grossularite (calcium-aluminum), and andradite (calcium-iron). The largest garnet mine in the world is a metamorphic deposit of almandite in east-central New York, where crystals as large as three feet in diameter have been recovered; the product is used as an abrasive on hard wood and other materials.

# 6

# How Rocks Are Classified

Rocks, unlike minerals, represent almost all gradations from one extreme of texture and composition to the opposite extreme. If a sufficiently large and varied number of rock specimens were brought together, they could be arranged to show barely perceptible transitions in almost every direction. Certain gaps would be unfilled and they would be conspicuous by contrast—such missing sections of the rock series are puzzling to petrologists who otherwise find the natural sequence to be orderly and gradual. Because of this nearly uninterrupted continuity among rocks, the names given to them are defined arbitrarily and the limits are drawn artificially. Consequently, hundreds of useless rock names invented by overly eager geologists clutter up the literature.

Many rocks have been named according to the locality from which they were first described. The present name, however, may have little to do with any geographic place. In some instances the original name has later been given a more exact definition, thereby limiting it to rocks actually different from those occurring at the type locality. The important rock called syenite was so named by Werner because he considered the material that he described from Saxony to be the same as the famous monumental rock from Syene, near Aswan, Egypt—but the Egyptian rock is really granite.

Rocks have also been named after persons, such as charnockite; Job Charnock, not a geologist, was the founder of Calcutta and his tomb is made of this rock. Other rocks are named from their mineral composition, such as quartzite, which consists chiefly of quartz. Still others are named from their chemical composition, such as limestone, which is calcium carbonate, a compound of calcium oxide (lime) and carbon dioxide. The grain size gives the name to some rocks, such as sandstone, which consists of particles the size of sand. Various physical features are responsible for the naming of many rocks. such as soapstone (because of its smoothness) and pitchstone (because of its luster). Other aspects of their appearance, nature, or history also lie behind the names of rocks.

The term quartzite mentioned above is an example of a rock name having a popular usage different from its strictly scientific meaning; this word should probably be applied only to the metamorphosed (thoroughly changed) equivalent of a sandstone, but it is often carelessly used in reference to any tightly cemented sandstone—both rocks, however, are hard and durable.

Some rock names are used commercially in a way that differs from their scientific meaning. For example, in the monumental-stone industry marble sometimes refers to limestone or dolomite, as well as to true marble, which is their metamorphic equivalent. Similarly, the granite of trade may be true granite, but just as likely it could be one of several related rocks resembling granite.

The over-all classification of rocks divides them into igneous, sedimentary, and metamorphic rocks. The origin of each of these three major kinds is described in Chapter 5. Within each type are many subdivisions, with gradations between them.

Rocks can be classified either *megascopically,* that is, by observation in the outcrop or in a hand specimen, or *microscopically,* in "thin sections" under a microscope. Each serves its own purpose. A field classification provides a simplified way of identifying rocks outdoors, aided by nothing more than a hand lens and a bottle of acid to test the carbonate content. The best classifications of this sort—one is given in Table 1—are simple to interpret and easy to remember.

Because so many more kinds of minerals can be identified with a microscope in the laboratory than by eye examination alone, this method of classification can be extremely complex, confused as it is by the introduction of superfluous names based upon minor variations. A *thin section* is a slice of rock mounted on a glass slide and ground to a standard thickness of nearly .03 millimeters, after which it is protected by a cover glass. So thin is it that most minerals in the slide become transparent and can be studied by their effect on the polarized light that a petrographic microscope transmits. Only the metallic minerals such as pyrite and magnetite remain opaque.

## CLASSIFICATION OF IGNEOUS ROCKS

Igneous rocks are classified according to their textures and minerals. Although the boundaries between the rock types are placed arbitrarily, these factors of texture and mineral composition are natural ones and they have a significance beyond that of mere description. The texture, for instance, is an indication of the geological conditions of temperature, pressure, depth, and chemical composition, as explained in Chapter 5. More specifically, texture is a reflection of the rate of cooling—coarse texture from slow cooling, fine texture from rapid cooling, porphyritic texture probably from a combination of both.

The mineral composition, on the other hand, depends primarily upon the chemical composition of the molten material from which igneous rocks are formed. If the minerals in a rock are known, the chemical composition is not difficult to calculate; but the reverse is not true, because different minerals in various proportions may crystallize out of the same magma or lava. Granite and obsidian, for instance, look very unlike—one containing quartz, feldspar, and other minerals, the other consisting almost solely of vol-

# TABLE 1

## SIMPLIFIED FIELD CLASSIFICATION OF IGNEOUS ROCKS

| Texture | Light Colored or Light Weight (Principal minerals: quartz and feldspar) | Intermediate (Principal minerals: feldspar, amphibole, biotite, pyroxene) | Dark Colored or Heavy Weight (Principal minerals: pyroxene, feldspar, amphibole, olivine) |
|---|---|---|---|
| Coarse grained | Granite<br>  Coarser: pegmatite<br>  Finer: aplite<br>  No quartz: syenite | Diorite<br>  With quartz: quartz diorite<br>  2 feldspars: monzonite<br>  With quartz: quartz monzonite, granodionite | Gabbro<br>  Olivine and pyroxene: peridotite |
| Fine grained | Felsite | Felsite | Basalt |
| Mixed grained | Granite porphyry, syenite porphyry, felsite porphyry | Diorite porphyry, etc., felsite porphyry | Basalt porphyry |
| Glassy | Obsidian<br>  Porous: pumice | Obsidian<br>  Porous: pumice | Basalt glass<br>  Porous: scoria |
| Broken | | ⟵———— Breccia, agglomerate, tuff ————⟶ | |

98     *Rocks and Minerals*

canic glass; yet they may have virtually identical amounts of silica, aluminum, and other chemical constituents. The difference is a result of the geologic conditions under which they came into being: granite, deep in the crust of the earth; obsidian, at or near the surface. Hence texture and composition must be employed together in order to determine the name of the rock.

The chemical composition of igneous rocks ranges from acidic to basic, as these terms are used in geology rather than more definitely in chemistry. Acidic rocks are also called silicic because of their high content of silica; when an excess of silica is present, free quartz usually forms. These rocks are generally light colored and light in weight. Granite is a typical example. Basic rocks, at the other end of the scale, are deficient in silica but contain large amounts of iron and magnesium. They are dark and heavy. Gabbro is an example of a basic rock. Intermediate rocks, such as diorite, stand between the two limits.

The above examples are all coarse-grained rocks, having originated at considerable depth. Their texture is called by several names, including *granitic* and *phaneritic*. When cooled more quickly, the same molten matter yields the fine-grained textures known as *aphanitic*. The equivalent of granite is rhyolite, that of diorite is andesite, that of gabbro is basalt.

Inasmuch as the individual minerals in a fine-grained rock cannot ordinarily be recognized in a hand specimen because they are too small, the aphanitic rocks are not so minutely subdivided as are the coarser rocks. A term such as felsite is hence necessary for field use, in order to compensate for our inability to make a closer identification without a microscope.

A *glassy* texture is easy to recognize. Even though they may appear to consist entirely of glass, rocks exhibiting this texture invariably reveal traces of tiny crystals when examined with a microscope. Obsidian is the commonest natural glass.

Any of these three chief types of igneous-rock textures may be modified by the presence of larger grains called phenocrysts, which presumably originate during an early stage of crystallization.

A fourth texture is known as *fragmental,* resulting from the explosion of a volcano when it tears apart its throat and rips pieces from the surrounding rock as the gas attempts to escape. The shattered product is often called pyroclastic and includes volcanic bombs, tuff, and breccia.

## CLASSIFICATION OF SEDIMENTARY ROCKS

Although they have originated in many ways and involve an almost endless variety of mineral and rock mixtures, sedimentary rocks bear fewer names than igneous rocks. Usually a single outstanding feature is the basis for the name applied, additional terms being supplied to describe special types more fully. Thus, a sandstone may also be a limey sandstone if it contains calcium carbonate as an impurity or cementing agent, or an arkosic sandstone if it is characterized by a large proportion of feldspar.

Considering the variations possible among them, the sedimentary rocks are often surprisingly pure. Nevertheless, they can grade from one end-member to another. Nearly pure sandstone, limestone, and shale are not at all rare, while a combination of any two of these principal components gives us sandy limestone or limey sandstone, sandy shale or shaly sandstone, limey shale or shaly limestone—depending upon which is the dominant constituent and which the modifying one. Likewise some of these rocks grade in texture from small grain size to large; a familiar series is siltstone-sandstone-conglomerate.

The descriptive terms given to sedimentary rocks refer to composition (as carbonaceous limestone, containing enough organic matter to be black or dark gray), or to texture (as arenaceous shale, including coarser particles the size of sand), or to origin (as biogenic limestone, formed

TABLE 2

## SIMPLIFIED FIELD CLASSIFICATION OF SEDIMENTARY ROCKS

| Classified by Composition | Rock | Classified by Origin | Rock |
|---|---|---|---|
| Recognizable particles: | | | |
| Coarse or mixed particles | | | |
| Rounded | Conglomerate | | |
| Angular | Breccia | Glacial deposition | Tillite |
| | | Hillslope weathering | Talus breccia |
| Medium to small particles | Sandstone | | |
| Much feldspar | Arkose | | |
| Shells | Limestone | | |
| Indistinguishable particles: | | | |
| Sand | Siltstone | Wind deposition | Loess |
| Mud | Shale | Hot-spring deposition | |
| Lime and clay | Marl | Carbonate | Travertine |
| Clay | Clay | Silica | Geyserite |
| Calcium carbonate | Limestone | | |
| Silica | Diatomaceous earth | | |
| Vegetable carbon | Coal | | |
| Salt | Rock salt | | |
| Calcium sulfate | Anhydrite | | |
| Hydrous calcium sulfate | Gypsum | | |
| Phosphate | Phosphate rock | | |

by organic action), to environment (as marine shale, deposited in sea water), or to coherence (as friable sandstone, crumbling easily), or to structure (as oölitic limestone, consisting of small rounded particles). Certain sedimentary rocks are so precisely named that their composition or origin can be pictured readily. Though tillite, for example, is the most heterogeneous of all rocks because it is the result of the haphazard dumping of glacial debris of every kind and size by the melting ice, the name conveys a definite connotation. Other examples are coquina, a porous rock

built up of shells; and loess, a wind deposit of silt and clay
—both recognized at sight for their distinctive appearance.

## CLASSIFICATION OF METAMORPHIC ROCKS

Attempts are made to classify metamorphic rocks according to the original material from which they were derived,
the kind of metamorphism that has taken place, and the
degree to which it has been effective. However, not all of
these factors involved in metamorphism are adequately
known for each rock, and so the features that can be determined with a reasonable degree of accuracy must be relied
upon instead. Depending, therefore, upon the minerals that
are present and the visible textures and structures, the usual
classification of metamorphic rocks is a fairly simple one.
These rocks can be differentiated according to whether they
show a parallel structure, as gneiss, or are massive, as marble.
(Often, however, this effect is not revealed without a microscope.) Emphasis on texture then separates the generally
coarsely banded gneiss from the more finely banded schist.
Further classification on the grounds of the prevailing min-

TABLE 3

**SIMPLIFIED FIELD CLASSIFICATION OF
METAMORPHIC ROCKS**

|  | Principal Mineral | Rock |
|---|---|---|
| **Parallel Structure** | Feldspar, quartz, other silicate minerals<br>Silicate minerals<br>Fine-grained silicate minerals | Gneiss<br>Schist<br>Slate |
| **Massive Structure** | Quartz<br>Calcite or dolomite<br>Serpentine<br>Talc<br>Clay<br>Hornblende | Quartzite<br>Marble<br>Serpentine<br>Soapstone<br>Hornfels<br>Amphibolite |

eral content distinguishes hornblende-gneiss from biotite-
gneiss.

## CLASSIFICATION OF ROCKS ACCORDING
## TO AGE

Another, very different method of classifying rocks is
based upon their age. True, analysis of age has been used
in an attempt to separate younger from older rocks of the
same kind, for example rhyolite and aporhyolite, but it has
not been successful and hence has been dropped. Even so,
a well-known contemporary geologist suggests that Pre-
Cambrian rocks—those of the earliest geologic time—can be
recognized because they "look old!" Establishing the age of
a rock may, nevertheless, have a much greater significance
than that of merely attaching a date to it, no matter how
accurately. Knowing the age of a rock places it within a
framework of related geologic events and fits it into its
proper niche in the long history of our planet—the rise of
continents, the disappearance of mountain ranges, the
changing patterns of land and sea during the vast sweep
of earth history.

Sedimentary rocks have been studied for their relative
ages ever since Nicolaus Steno in 1669 first stated the principle (called the law of superposition) that the strata at
the bottom of an undisturbed series are older than those
above them, for the same reason that when a number of
books are placed one at a time upon a table, the first book
will be at the bottom of the stack and the last one at the
top.

The more specific age of sedimentary rocks is determined
by the fossils found in them. These remains or impressions
of ancient plants and animals are indications of age because each group of strata contains its own characteristic
assemblage of fossils, which have evolved from older forms
that will therefore be found only at a lower level unless the
rocks have been displaced. The French naturalists Georges

Cuvier and Alexandre Brongiart first established this important principle through their work in the Paris basin during the beginning years of the nineteenth century. They, and William Smith in England, discovered the fact that the fossil sequence depends upon the age, the fossils from the lower and older beds being less like the animals and plants now living than are the fossils in the higher and younger beds, which come closer to our own time. Furthermore, rocks of the same age can be correlated across wide distances by their fossil content.

In spite of the remarkable stories that sedimentary rocks can tell, their dates are not calibrated in actual years. Such a more precise method of age determination is available only for igneous rocks. The spontaneous disintegration of uranium—its radioactivity—begins with the crystallization of uranium-bearing minerals from molten rock; eventually the uranium will be transformed into lead, as explained in Chapter 10. Half of the original amount of uranium will become lead in 7,600 million years. Determining the uranium-lead ratio by complex analyses therefore gives the time that has elapsed since the solidification of the rock.

The science of historical geology shows, by the positions of rock layers with respect to one another, the time relationships that exist among bodies of rock—both igneous and sedimentary, and metamorphic rocks as well. A rock dike that has forced its way into other rocks must be younger than they; a rock inclusion that is surrounded by another rock is evidently the older; and there are other similar generalizations.

Geologic time started when the ordinary geologic processes were initiated on the newly created earth. How long ago this happened is not known; the age of the oldest rocks is being pushed further and further back as additional evidence continues to be turned up. The geologic time scale, showing the classification of rocks by age, is given in Table 4.

The largest divisions of geologic time are called *eras* and

TABLE  4

## GEOLOGIC TIME SCALE

| Era | Period | Epoch | Duration in Millions of Years | Began Millions of Years Ago |
|-----|--------|-------|-------------------------------|-----------------------------|
| Cenozoic | Quaternary | Recent | (Late archeo-logic and his-toric time) | |
| | | Pleistocene | 1 | 1 |
| | Tertiary | Pliocene | 12 | 13 |
| | | Miocene | 12 | 25 |
| | | Oligocene | 11 | 36 |
| | | Eocene | 22 | 58 |
| | | Paleocene | 5 | 63 |
| Mesozoic | Cretaceous | | 72 | 135 |
| | Jurassic | | 46 | 181 |
| | Triassic | | 49 | 230 |
| Paleozoic | Permian | | 50 | 280 |
| | Carboniferous: Pennsylvanian and Mississippian | | 65 | 345 |
| | Devonian | | 60 | 405 |
| | Silurian | | 20 | 425 |
| | Ordovician | | 75 | 500 |
| | Cambrian | | 100 | 600 |
| Pre-Cambrian: Proterozoic and Archeozoic | | | 900 (Undetermined) | 1,500 |

are separated from one another by major mountain-making occurrences, probably world-wide in scope. These events are referred to as *revolutions,* owing to the profound effect they presumably had upon the earth and its inhabitants.

Eras are subdivided into *periods,* which are separated from one another by regional mountain-making events called *disturbances,* accompanied by extensive withdrawals of the sea from the low parts of the continents which they seem to inundate repeatedly. The more recent periods are further divided into *epochs,* which are separated by retreats of the sea on a regional scale.

TABLE 4—*Continued*

## GEOLOGIC TIME SCALE

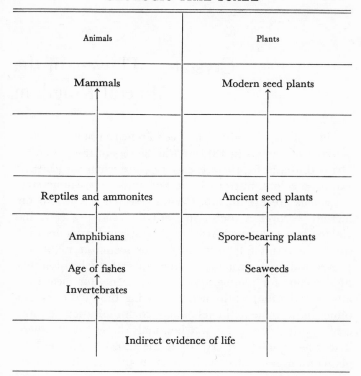

|  Animals  |  Plants  |
|-----------|----------|
| Mammals | Modern seed plants |
| Reptiles and ammonites | Ancient seed plants |
| Amphibians | Spore-bearing plants |
| Age of fishes | Seaweeds |
| Invertebrates |  |
| Indirect evidence of life | |

Since, moreover, the evolution of organisms is substantially affected by the changing environment, the divisions of geologic time also correspond to natural breaks in the stream of life.

The names of the eras, periods, and epochs have various derivations. The Cambrian period, for instance, is named from the Roman name for Wales, where rocks of this age were first studied. Cretaceous signifies the chalk deposits of the Chalk Cliffs of England and France. Mesozoic means "middle life," in allusion to the medieval-like dinosaurs and other animals of that time.

# 7

# Crystals—Flowers of the Mineral Kingdom

Abbé Haüy, the gifted pioneer French crystallographer, referred to crystals in 1817 as "the flowers of the minerals." His enthusiasm for them is easy to share when we see their exquisite colors, lustrous faces, and satisfying symmetry.

Crystals are useful, too. Crystal research has led to numerous discoveries useful in both war and peace. It has yielded gun sights and hearing aids, apparatus for locating submarines and fish, instruments for seeing at night, improved radio performance, picture tubes for television sets, light meters for photographers, instruments for measuring atomic radiation, equipment for testing the quality of gasoline, improvements in telephone communication, fluorescent lighting, jewels for watches, and a long list of others. The latest miracle in crystals is the transistor, a speck of germanium embedded with wires in plastic; although requiring no heated filament or vacuum, no warm-up and little power, it is able to perform dependably many of the functions of a vacuum tube while oscillating in excess of 300 million times a second!

The word crystal was first applied to clear quartz, which the Greek philosophers believed to be water congealed into a six-sided solid body by the intense cold of the Alps. Historically, therefore, the rock-crystal variety of quartz is the original of all crystals.

The visible body of a crystal is the outward evidence of a definite, orderly arrangement of the atoms inside. These tiny particles are held together by electrical attraction, usually that of oppositely charged (positive and negative) units called ions. They are systematically distributed in all directions throughout the entire crystal, building into a three-dimensional pattern called a crystal lattice. The design of the lattice determines the outward form of the crystal and its other essential properties.

Most minerals develop into crystals, for this is the normal condition of a chemical substance (either natural or artificial) when it solidifies from a liquid or gas. This is the condition of least energy and hence greatest stability. As more of the same material is added, a crystal grows in size like a living organism, except that the process is by accumulation from the outside rather than expansion from within. Growth is usually slow, taking perhaps as long as thousands of years, but sometimes it may be rapid enough to observe from day to day. Crystals begin in size with invisible ones that can be seen only through an ultramicroscope and range on up to giants that weigh a number of tons. The native home of huge crystals is the rock known as pegmatite, to which Chapter 9 is devoted.

A few years ago Dr. Charles Palache, the eminent mineralogist, published statistics about the largest known crystals of certain minerals. Puzzled by the extraordinary concentration at one place of the needed chemical constituents and by the apparent uniformity of the environment during long periods of time, he asked the still-unanswered question: "How do such crystals support their own weight during growth and how do they maintain their shape?" Dr. Clifford Frondel and others since then have recorded additional data on large crystals.

Probably the greatest crystals ever found were of feldspar, observed in Karelia in the Soviet Union. Thousands of tons of this mineral were mined here from each of several individual crystals. From Maine have been reported crystals of microcline feldspar "up to 20 feet across."

The champions among American crystals are those of spodumene taken from the Etta mine near Keystone, South

Dakota. The heaviest of them reached a weight of 90 tons and was 42 feet long. Many others approaching 20 feet in length can still be seen embedded in the walls of this noted quarry, where they resemble the bleached and cracked trunks of trees. A close competitor to the record-holder was a crystal of phlogopite mica in the Lacy mine in Ontario. About the same weight as the big spodumene, it was 33 feet long and 14 feet across, and it trimmed to 60 tons of useful mica. All of these enormous minerals occurred in pegmatite.

Some minerals grow into crystals only on special occasions, even though they may have the requisite atomic structure. Instead they are "massive" or take on various imitative outlines or mineral "habits," as described on page 36. Bornite, for example, is a common enough mineral, an ore of copper, but crystals of it are quite rare. A few minerals, such as opal, and certain inorganic chemical compounds, such as obsidian, which is volcanic glass, do not crystallize at all; their atoms have come together in random positions and they are said to be noncrystalline or amorphous.

The larger a crystal grows, the more apt it is to lose its ideal perfection, just as an older person has had more time than a younger one to acquire bad traits of character. The crystal faces become distorted or etched, inclusions reduce the transparency, and other imperfections appear. Crystals of microscopic size show the highest development of clarity and symmetry.

The most dependable feature of any crystal is the constancy of the angles between corresponding faces. Nicolaus Steno, a Danish physician living in Florence, first discovered this principle in 1668 after he had experimented with specimens of quartz from many different localities. The faces on a crystal are mathematically related to one another, and the same measurements apply to all specimens of the same kind, no matter what the size or where the occurrence. For example, the outer angle between adjacent faces at the end of a quartz crystal is always $226°$ $16'$, whether the crystal is a tiny purple one from Switzerland or a 50-pound colorless one from Brazil. Crystal angles are measured with a simple protractor or an elaborate instrument called an optical goniometer.

A "form" comprises all similar faces on a crystal. Thus, all the cube faces on a crystal of pyrite—there will be six if the crystal is complete—belong to the same form. Each face that is present on a crystal interferes with the growth of some other face. As one face enlarges at the expense of another, their relative sizes change, and an endless diversity of appearance becomes possible. Crystals, we can be sure, have as infinite a variety as Cleopatra.

A significant feature of the majority of crystals is that most of their properties vary according to the crystal direction. Parallel directions in a whole crystal or in any fragment of it have identical physical characteristics, such as transmission of light, conduction of electricity, and all the rest—for they are controlled by the same atomic structure that produces the crystal forms. A curious illustration, but entirely normal, is the change in color of the mineral cordierite, which may be yellow when viewed through the length of the crystal but blue or violet across the width.

## CRYSTAL SYSTEMS

Crystals can, of course, be classified in more than one way. The most general classification is based upon the arrangement of axes within the crystal, yielding six main divisions called crystal systems. Although the axes are imaginary lines, like the equator on the earth, they are none the less useful in describing crystals. The number, position, and relative lengths of the axes distinguish the six crystal systems from one another. The names of many crystals can be identified by determining these facts about their axes and looking them up in appropriate tables. The six systems, described below, may further be subdivided into 32 crystal classes or 230 space-groups, according to the internal symmetry.

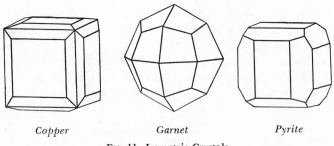

*Copper*          *Garnet*          *Pyrite*

Fig. 11—Isometric Crystals.

**Isometric.** Isometric crystals have three axes, which have equal lengths and meet in the center at right angles.

Common table salt, which is the same as the mineral halite, is a typical example of an isometric crystal. Under a magnifying glass the glistening little cubes reveal equal sides and equal angles, corresponding to the word isometric, which means "equal measure." This statement is true of all members of this system, even when the crystal form is not a simple cube. Diamond, for instance, usually occurs in an octahedron which resembles two square pyramids placed base to base, but the sides and angles rigidly conform to the requirements.

The dodecahedron and trapezohedron are other common isometric forms, and there are numerous others, some with formidable names, such as left-handed pentagonal icositetrahedron, which can be used to frighten naughty children. These forms frequently exist in combination with one another. Some modifications are so complex that rare crystals may have one hundred or more minute faces and so be practically round. Most isometric crystals found in stream deposits are more or less equidimensional at the start, tending to become almost spherical pebbles as they are subjected to continued erosion. Isometric crystals are also recognized by their generally having square or triangular faces.

Halite crystals sometimes have a cavernous or hopper-shaped appearance. Galena, another common isometric mineral, often shows curious skeletal crystals, as though parts had been dissolved, leaving the rest standing in sharp projections. Chalcotrichite, an attractive variety of cuprite, sometimes consists of cubes that have been elongated so far in one direction as to resemble needles or hairs. Crystals of gold, silver, and copper, all of which are isometric, often develop amazingly twisted and wirelike configurations, some delicate, and some grotesque.

Garnet is a group of minerals that display excellent isometric crystals in the form of trapezohedrons. The operators of the Barton garnet deposit at Gore Mountain, New York, have recovered individual crystals 3 feet in diameter. Perhaps the most extreme development of all known isometric crystals are those that occur as garnet boulders on the shore of Dalsfjord, Norway; the estimated weight of the largest was 1,540 pounds.

Analcime and leucite, both referred to as "white garnet," are two other silicate minerals having trapezohedral crystals. Magnetite and franklinite are metallic minerals occurring in excellent octahedrons. The superb cubes of fluorite are outstanding among isometric crystals. Pyrite also appears in cubes and in a special form that is so characteristic of it that it is called a pyritohedron. Sphalerite, chromite, and uraninite are other important minerals that crystallize in the isometric system.

**Tetragonal.** Tetragonal crystals have three axes, which meet in the center at right angles; the two horizontal axes have equal lengths, the vertical one being either longer or

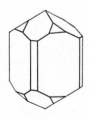
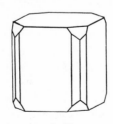
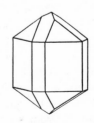

*Rutile*          *Apophyllite*          *Cassiterite*

Fig. 12—Tetragonal Crystals.

shorter than the others. The principle of a tetragonal crystal can be arrived at by considering an isometric crystal stretched or flattened along the upright axis. The common tetragonal minerals (except chalcopyrite) have a square outline when viewed from the top. Chalcopyrite (an important copper-iron sulfide) is an exception, being wedge-shaped, but it fulfills the technical requirements for this system.

Long square crystals with pointed ends are familiar among tetragonal minerals. Cassiterite, idocrase, scapolite, and apophyllite are good examples. Rutile, however, is frequently found in exceedingly long and slender needlelike crystals; specimens of quartz with rutile inclusions look as though they had been shot through with small red arrows. Crystals of yellow wulfenite, on the contrary, are often so flat that they resemble thin chips of butterscotch candy.

**Hexagonal.** Hexagonal crystals have four axes, three of which are horizontal and have equal lengths, meeting in the center at 120-degree angles; the vertical one, at right angles to the others, is either longer or shorter than they. A hexagonal crystal can be derived from a tetragonal one by imagining the square outline modified to a six-sided one, with an extra horizontal axis provided. The shape of such a crystal usually reveals the group to which it belongs. Certain crystals—most conspicuously tourmaline—have a triangular outline, as alternate faces have developed to dominate the figure. Most hexagonal crystals are longer in the vertical direction, only a few—such as graphite, ilmenite, and hematite—being flattened.

This system embraces some of the finest, largest, and most abundant of all crystals. Beryl, corundum, quartz, apatite, and calcite are among the minerals most remarkable for their outstanding size. A calcite crystal from Sterling Bush, New York, weighed about 1,000 pounds and measured 43 inches from top to base. No crystals are more multifarious than those of calcite, over 300 different forms having been recorded. Tourmaline crystals are distinctive on account of

Fig. 13—Lustrous calcite crystals from Cumberland, England, are highly prized by mineral collectors and museums. (*Courtesy of Ward's Natural Science Establishment.*)

their triangular shape. Ice belongs here, too, though only in freshly fallen snow is the intricate hexagonal pattern evident.

Quartz is the best-known hexagonal mineral, native to every sort of geologic environment and constituting about 12 per cent of the earth's crust. Although quartz is found in many kinds of rock, superb crystals of the quality that adorns a mineral cabinet have originated in cavities, where they were deposited from solutions circulating beneath the surface, often at great depths. From such an opening, or

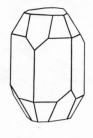

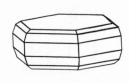

*Corundum*          *Pyrrhotite*          *Calcite*

Fig. 14—Hexagonal Crystals.

pocket, came the gigantic smoky quartz crystals found in Switzerland in 1867; many individuals weighed between 200 and 250 pounds each. Another specimen from the Alps, this one of ordinary quartz—though hardly an ordinary crystal!—is estimated at 870 pounds. A Siberian quartz crystal as tall as a two-story building was reported in 1959.

A readily noticed characteristic of quartz is the series of horizontal lines that run across the front faces. These are evidence of a struggle that went on within the growing crystal, a conflict between two opposing forms. First the growth proceeded for a time in one direction, then in another, returning again to the first. Each shifting left its mark as a fine line parallel to the one next to it—these are called striations.

Other important minerals that crystallize in the hexagonal system include a group of carbonates related to calcite—dolomite, magnesite, siderite, rhodochrosite, and smithsonite. Some of these, however, are much more common in massive specimens than in crystals.

**Orthorhombic.** Orthorhombic crystals have three axes, which meet in the center at right angles, each having a different length. If a tetragonal crystal could be stretched or flattened along one of its horizontal axes, all three axes would then be of unequal lengths and the orthorhombic symmetry would be produced. The outline of such crystals is generally a rectangle, perhaps with the edges cut off. Most orthorhombic crystals are considerably higher than they are wide, though some are short and stubby (such as

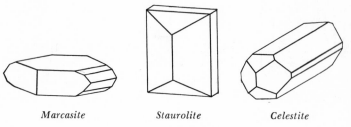

*Marcasite*     *Staurolite*     *Celestite*

Fig. 15—Orthorhombic Crystals.

sulfur), and a few are flat and thin (such as barite and celestite), although one transparent barite crystal from the Dufton lead mines in Westmorland, England, weighed 100 pounds.

Topaz is one of the most beautifully crystallized of all minerals. Its orthorhombic crystals are often remarkably complex, and they have a peculiar slippery feel that is truly individual.

Among the other important orthorhombic minerals are olivine, arsenopyrite, staurolite, aragonite, andalusite, chrys-oberyl, and stibnite. Examples of the wonderful Japanese crystals of stibnite as much as 2 feet long are in the Harvard Mineralogical Museum. Brookite is an orthorhombic mineral found only in crystal form.

**Monoclinic.** Monoclinic crystals have three axes, each having a different length; two of them meet at right angles, the other being inclined forward and downward. The monoclinic pattern might be obtained from the orthorhombic one by slanting downward the front-to-back axis. This gives monoclinic crystals a tilted-forward look, so well shown in gypsum.

The immense crystals of spodumene in the Black Hills of South Dakota rank among the world's largest crystals. They are deeply grooved and furrowed along their length.

Several of the essential minerals of igneous rocks belong to the monoclinic system. Orthoclase feldspar and the mica,

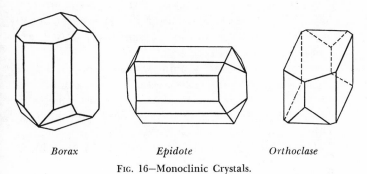

*Borax*          *Epidote*          *Orthoclase*

Fig. 16—Monoclinic Crystals.

amphibole, and pyroxene groups all exhibit well-developed crystals.

Borax and monazite, the primary sources of the radioactive element thorium, are other important minerals with typical monoclinic forms. Wolframite, an iron-manganese-tungsten mineral, has the only good metallic crystals in this system.

**Triclinic.** Triclinic crystals have three axes, which meet in the center at oblique angles and have different lengths. A triclinic crystal might be derived from a monoclinic one by pushing askew the front-to-back axis. The result would

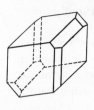   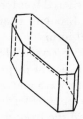   

*Axinite*          *Chalcanthite*          *Rhodonite*

FIG. 17—Triclinic Crystals.

be a total lack of any evident symmetry. Hence triclinic crystals have an over-all "lopsided" appearance, which is a most useful clue to the identification of well-developed crystals.

They are also recognized by the fact that no more than two similar faces are ever present on the same specimen; in other words, each form consists solely of two parallel faces on opposite sides of the specimen.

No metallic crystals are prominent in the triclinic system. Microcline feldspar and the exceedingly important series of plagioclase feldspars are triclinic. So also are the large, coarse crystals of amblygonite and rhodonite, and the long, roughly-bladed crystals of kyanite. Axinite is so named because its triclinic crystals are wedge-shaped, like the blade of an axe.

## CRYSTAL GROUPS

Natural crystals are more apt to occur in groups than in lone individuals. The mineral-bearing solutions begin to crystallize at a number of separate but nearby places, each of which then acts as a center for a growing crystal.

Frequently crystals of the same kind are built up in parallel positions that give a general symmetry and an especial attractiveness to the group. Others are intergrown in haphazard and strange ways, depending upon accidental condi-

Fig. 18—"Sand crystals," composed of calcite roughly crystallized around loose grains of sand. Snake Buttes, South Dakota. (*Courtesy of Ward's Natural Science Establishment.*)

tions not always easy to interpret. Interesting also are the crystals that enclose others within them—either an earlier growth of the same kind, called a phantom because of its ghostly appearance, or an entirely different mineral. One of the countless examples of the latter type are the brilliant crystals of copper surrounded by calcite crystals from northern Michigan.

## TWIN CRYSTALS

When two or more crystals are united in some definite fashion, they are known as twin crystals. Adjacent parts interlock so that the atomic structure is shared in common. Some parts are parallel and others are in reverse positions. The manner in which they fit together is expressed by a so-called twin law, which indicates how one part would turn into the other by a simple act, such as rotating it 180 degrees or reflecting it in a mirror. In most instances, however, twin crystals actually grow as such from the beginning, and so the twin law is merely a geometrical description of the relationship between the individuals.

The most obvious and appealing of twin crystals are the natural crosses. The familiar "fairy crosses" which come chiefly from Georgia and New Mexico but which are sold as local souvenirs in every state, are twin crystals of the min-

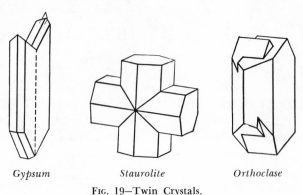

Gypsum                Staurolite              Orthoclase

Fig. 19—Twin Crystals.

eral staurolite, the parts penetrating each other almost exactly at right angles. Latin and Greek crosses are both represented; other staurolite twins are oriented at sharper angles to resemble the letter *X*. Curious twin crystals of pyrite are called iron crosses, having to some extent the shape of a Maltese cross when viewed from certain positions.

Gypsum very often develops into double crystals with one end notched like the letter *M*. These are called swallow-tail twins and they represent two parts that are in contact, instead of penetrating each other as did the others just mentioned. The halves of cassiterite twins come together in a notch which resembles the visor of a cap, and so the crystals are called visor twins. Rutile and zircon twins are often shaped like a bent arm or leg and thus are called elbow or knee twins. The numerous varieties of twinning in calcite and quartz go under names such as butterfly, Japanese, and Brazil twins.

When twinning is repeated several times, a somewhat circular or starlike crystal may be produced. Chrysoberyl, rutile, and cerussite are among the minerals growing in this attractive manner. Six-sided disks of twinned aragonite, known as Indian dollars to the early settlers, are found in abundance along the foothills of the Rocky Mountains in Colorado.

The plagioclase series of feldspars are especially good examples of repeated twinning on a prolific scale, giving rise to numerous striations on the surface. These thin parallel lines help us greatly to recognize the minerals in hand specimens and to distinguish the members of the series under a microscope.

## PSEUDOMORPHS—CRYSTALS IN DISGUISE

On the one hand, crystal form is a highly valuable aid in the identification of minerals. On the other hand, it can be equally misleading, for many crystals adopt disguises that conceal rather than reveal their true nature. Such a mas-

Fig. 20—Petrified wood, in which the woody structure has been replaced by silica. Castle Dome, Arizona. (*Courtesy of Ward's Natural Science Establishment.*)

querade takes place when a mineral changes into another mineral in every respect except its outer form, which stays the same. The original outline is thereby preserved, but the chemical composition and physical properties now belong to the new mineral. Such a transformation produces what is called a pseudomorph, a word meaning false form.

Petrified wood is probably the best-known example of the change of a substance to a mineral pseudomorph. The chalcedony variety of quartz has now replaced the former wood fiber. Crystal pseudomorphs include the numerous cubes of pyrite (iron sulfide) that have altered to cubes of goethite (hydrous iron oxide), and are referred to as "pseudomorphs of goethite after pyrite." Exceptional specimens of this kind are found at Pelican Point, Utah. Beautiful crystals of blue azurite change readily to green malachite by means of a slight loss of carbon dioxide and a gain in water content. Hard minerals can yield to soft ones, as when corundum becomes talc in everything but shape, which is still the hexagonal pattern of corundum.

Of all the various kinds of minerals, those that are most likely to occur in good crystals are the gems, described in Chapter 8. The rare perfection that constitutes the very essence of a gem is favored by the growth of distinct crystals.

# 8

# The Realm of Gems

Of all the members of the mineral kingdom, gems have the most universal appeal. For their bright colors and intriguing forms, they were the earliest to attract the attention of man. Supernatural powers were ascribed to unusual stones by the primitive peoples who found them in stream beds or on open ground or near the entrance to the caves in which they sought shelter and safety. Whichever use of gems came first—as ornaments to adorn the body, or as amulets and charms to calm the superstitious mind—both benefits were doubtless soon conferred by the same specimen.

Amulets of undeniable authenticity were made from gems and even common stones by marking them with images and prayers. Long beads called cylinders, pierced lengthwise for stringing, were carved with these figures and inscriptions, and sometimes they were also used as seals. Scarabs, which were representations of a beetle, symbol of the immortality of the soul, gained prominence in Egypt about the time of the ninth dynasty. They were employed both as seals and as amulets.

Birthstones seem to have been worn first in Germany or Poland during the sixteenth century. The signs of the zodiac rather than the months of the calendar decided the particular gem that was to be favored. This custom of birthstones can be traced back to the breastplate of judgment worn by the high priest, as described in Exodus 28; it was adorned with twelve gems, each engraved with the name of one of the tribes of Israel. A similar idea but with a different series of gems appears in the New Testament, where (in the 21st chapter of the Book of Revelation or the Apocalypse) twelve gems, each inscribed with the name of an apostle, constituted the foundation stones of the holy city, New Jerusalem.

Tracing the identity of the gems mentioned in the Bible and other ancient writings is a confusing problem, owing to the similar appearance of some of them, to the difficulty of translating manuscripts, to errors in copying, and to changes in the gems that were actually used from time to time. Present-day lists of birthstones stem directly from the Biblical record, modified by the preferences of various races and nations.

Rough pebbles of gemmy minerals were, at first, merely drilled and strung as necklaces, probably the earliest kind of jewelry. Later the original forms usually were rounded, though natural crystal faces were often preserved as found. Improved techniques led gradually to the creation of the cylinder and scarab. A cylinder with the name of Sargon I of Babylonia, used as a seal, is said to date back to 3500 B.C. Beads were readily adapted to the making of armlets, though gem-set bracelets and metal rings had to wait for more advanced cultures.

More skill than was required for the earlier carving of cylinders and scarabs produced the exquisite craftsmanship of the Greek and Roman gem engravers. The small size and high value of the material at their disposal encouraged the development of a superior art, which has been faithfully preserved because of the durability of the medium in which they worked.

Cameos were introduced for decorative purposes about 300 B.C., as a contrast to the older forms called intaglios, which were incised below the surface and hence served also as seals.

With the decline of the classic era, gem engraving languished until its revival during the Renaissance. In the eighteenth century another renewal of interest in carved gems took place, but the results were less original than previously.

# THE ART OF THE LAPIDARY

The art of the lapidary has not only influenced the evolution of jewelry forms, but it has also been involved in some manner in the use of all the gems. Some mineralogists view the cutting and polishing process as essentially a disfigurement of natural material. And it is true that one who learns to appreciate fully the delicate coloring, wondrous symmetry, and curious sports of nature's handiwork will generally prefer not to molest them. For jewelry uses, however, the gem is rare that cannot be improved in beauty through adequate lapidary treatment. Pearl and staurolite are the only gems that are customarily worn in their original state, but even pearls are pierced for stringing into beads, and staurolite (the charming fairy-cross variety) for hanging on a chain.

The quality of cutting that it has undergone may play a considerable part in determining the value of a gem, for it can bring out the inherent possibilities to best advantage, whereas poor work can ruin even the finest stone.

The simplest style of cutting, known as cabochon, consists of rounded surfaces of varying degrees of curvature, culminating in an entirely round bead. Frequently the bottom of a cabochon stone is cut flat. Faceted gems, on the contrary, have only plane surfaces called facets. Carved and engraved stones may be characterized by a few basic strokes or by designs of the utmost intricacy.

The style of cutting that is used for a particular kind of gem is determined largely by the optical properties of the material. Transparent gems, therefore, are generally faceted so as to reveal best their clearness, brilliancy, and fire. Diamond is the pre-eminent example. Opaque and translucent gems, which depend for their beauty mostly upon an attractive color or interesting pattern, are more effectively fashioned as cabochons. Turquoise and agate fall into this catagory.

## KINDS OF GEMS

The realm of gems includes several precious substances—certain animal and vegetable products—that lie outside the mineral kingdom. Most gems, however, are true minerals. Of the 1,600 or more mineral species, the number depending upon the way in which minerals are classified, about 80 have been regarded as gems, though many of these are met with only occasionally. Diamond, the noblest of gems, is perhaps the most remarkable of all minerals.

A few gems are rocks. Such, for example, is lapis lazuli, the sapphire of the Bible, the most highly prized blue gem of ancient times. This rock consists of at least half a dozen individual minerals. The blue minerals, of which hauynite has been proved to be the most abundant, are members of the feldspathoid group and include lazurite, sodalite, and noselite. Spangling the rich blue background of lapis lazuli are golden flecks of pyrite and white wisps of calcite, the whole resembling (as Pliny described it) the star-bedecked night sky.

The kind of rock that is homogeneous throughout, varying chiefly in chemical composition, as described on page 4, is represented by three gems—obsidian, silica-glass, and tektite—the first two of which are natural glasses of volcanic origin, having wide ranges in their content of silica.

Four gems trace their ancestry to living things. Two of them, pearl and coral, are gems of the sea and have an animal origin, though they contain crystalline matter indistinguishable from ordinary minerals. Pearl is formed within certain mollusks which secrete the pearl-substance to line the shells in which they live. Coral consists of the axial skeletons of tiny marine animals called polyps, which live in branching colonies and extract calcium carbonate from the water to build their supporting structures, leaving them to accumulate after they die.

The other two organic gems, amber and jet, are gems of

the land and are derived from vegetation. Amber is the fossil resin of ancient conifer trees of the Tertiary period in geologic history. Jet is a black variety of lignite or brown coal—surely the blackest brown thing you have ever seen!

For countless centuries man has prepared substitutes for his favored gems in order to make them more abundant. The Egyptians were skilled manufacturers of gems and so were the Romans, especially in reproducing pearls in enormous quantities. Fine glass gems called paste became so popular in Europe that they were a fad among royalty and the wealthy. These imitations are like natural gems only in appearance and can be readily identified by their other characteristics.

The magic of modern science has made available still other kinds of man-made products, bearing an even closer resemblance to genuine gems. The most remarkable of these are the synthetic gems described in Chapter 16. Composite gems consist of several pieces combined to make a single, larger stone; their primary intent is to deceive, though often they serve a useful purpose by providing a surface that is harder than the original. Doublets and triplets, containing two or three parts cemented or fused together, either before or after being cut, are examples of composite gems. The most important doublet has a slice of precious black opal cemented onto a base of ordinary opal or black chalcedony (known as "black onyx"); such a method of strengthening black opal is necessary because this exquisite gem usually occurs in thin layers which scarcely cover the rock on which they are found.

Treated gems are those which have had their original color improved in salability by heat, chemicals, or radioactivity. Diamonds, for instance, turn green when exposed to radium emanations. A familiar practice in the Brazilian gem trade has been to heat smoky quartz, changing it into the more popular yellow quartz, called citrine. Probably all the beautiful blue, golden yellow, and diamondlike zircons that are sold in jewelry stores have been obtained by heating brown zircon. Excluding air from the charcoal furnace results in the blue variety; the presence of air gives the golden variety; colorless zircon can be produced either way.

Only one representative of a cultured gem is known—any pearl grown by artificially encouraging the oyster in its misfortunes. Without this interference it might have lived comfortably but barrenly in the depths of the sea. A miniature surgical operation is necessary to transfer a small bead, enclosed within a sac cut from one animal into the tissues of another one. To ease the discomfort the oyster coats the intrusion with its precious secretion; the pearls reach full growth in a total of ten years. Both before and after they are treated, the mollusks are kept in cages suspended from rafts in the water.

**Diamond, King of Gems.** The first diamonds came from India, the marketing center being Golconda. The Indian mines have yielded most of the famous stones of history. As the supply there diminished almost to extinction, diamonds were discovered about 1720 in Brazil, where the industry flourished for a century and a half. Then, as another decline set in, the prolific South African deposits came to light in the year 1867.

The desirable features of practically all the other gems are incorporated in diamond. This amazing mineral possesses hardness to a superlative degree; it flashes forth with the radiance of the sun and the splendor of the rainbow; it is rare enough to be much wanted, yet abundant enough so that the demand for it can be met. Even the lack of a color of its own is satisfied by the occasional colored diamond, which is indeed the rarest of all gems. The blue Hope, the orange Tiffany, and the Dresden Green diamonds are unrivaled.

In spite of its hardness, which exceeds that of any other substance, diamond can readily be cleaved in certain directions of weakness. This method of splitting a crystal enables the diamond cutter to remove flawed parts with little delay, reducing the rough stone to a convenient size. It is then sawed with a rapidly spinning bronze disk fed with a mixture of diamond dust and oil. A similar abrasive covers a horizontally rotating iron wheel which puts on the facets, performing the double task of cutting and polishing at one operation. A normal diamond of average size has 58 facets, 25 below the equator (called the girdle) and 33 above. Tiny or incompletely fashioned diamonds have fewer facets, whereas a very large or unusual stone may have extra facets to catch the light and break it up into its vivid rainbow hues.

Africa produces diamonds from two main sources. The original home of diamond is in a rock called kimberlite, which occurs in "pipes," these being the necks of ancient volcanoes. Erosion of this rock has carried its precious contents to accumulate elsewhere in alluvial or placer deposits. Besides a sporadic distribution in the southern half of the "dark continent," bodies of diamond-bearing kimberlite are also known in Pike County, Arkansas, but the high cost of production has limited the output of this treasure house and has caused it to become a tourist attraction instead.

The deepest of diamond mines is the Kimberley, which was opened below 4,000 feet, but other pipe mines cover larger areas and have yielded better and more numerous gems. Exceeding all previous and subsequent diamonds in size was the Cullinan, as large as a man's fist and weighing 3,106 carats. Little doubt exists that only the smaller half of a giant crystal was actually recovered.

The wheels of modern industry would slow appreciably if the gem diamond's prosaic cousin, the industrial diamond, were suddenly to disappear from the market. The pace of today's factories, mines, and wells is geared to the unequaled hardness and durability of this mineral, so strategic in peace and war. Industrial diamonds are used for truing grinding wheels, turning machine tools, drawing wire, drilling through rock, and a host of other purposes from engraving gem stones to shaping bowling balls.

Fig. 21—Kimberley Diamond mine, now surrounded by the city of Kimberley, South Africa. (Courtesy of De Beers Consolidated Mines, Ltd.)

**Pearl, Queen of Gems.** The soft shimmer of a pearl forms an ideal contrast to the scintillating luster of a diamond. The Queen of Gems, perfect in its naked beauty, needing no preparation or treatment except perhaps to be drilled for stringing, has been a favorite gem since earliest times.

Though not a gem stone, pearl contains mineral substances that resemble, except in their origin, certain common minerals. The pearl-bearing mollusk is a shellfish which secretes the precious material in order to ease an irritation aroused by the presence of a foreign substance. The animal extracts calcium carbonate from the water and uses it to construct its shell. This shell consists of three layers containing calcite, aragonite (both are minerals), and conchiolin, a brown material related to the chitin of which our fingernails are composed. The iridescent inner layer is known as mother-of-pearl; it corresponds closely to the outer surface of a pearl, which also has a rich but subdued sheen called "orient."

The pearl fisheries along the Arabian coast of the Persian Gulf have been worked for more than two thousand years. The northwest shore of Ceylon in the Gulf of Mannar is likewise an ancient and important source. The waters of northern and western Australia, the Sulu Sea northeast of Borneo, the shores of the Aru Islands southwest of New Guinea, and lagoons and outer waters of various South Pacific coral islands and atolls yield the most and the choicest of the Oriental pearls.

The warm waters of the Caribbean Sea and Gulf of Mexico also furnish valuable pearls. During many summers pearls have been recovered from oysters in the Mississippi and its tributaries. Streams in Scotland, Ireland, Wales, China, and Japan have for centuries produced such river pearls.

**Ruby and Sapphire, Gem Cousins.** The vivid red of ruby and the serene blue of sapphire are so dissimilar that it is difficult to realize how much alike the gems themselves really happen to be. They are in fact merely color varieties of a single mineral known as corundum. Only a small amount of metallic oxides, which are not even represented in the chemical formula of the corundum gems, can create a startling difference in their appearance.

Although ruby is red corundum and the word sapphire is popularly applied solely to the blue variety, the latter term is equally appropriate for the other exquisite colors that grace this versatile mineral. Thus there is the superb green sapphire, the splendid purple sapphire, the blazing golden sapphire. Pink sapphire grades imperceptibly into ruby, the distinction between them being virtually imaginary. So it is with the other varieties, which unfold in a continuous panorama from the plain colorless stone called white sapphire to those which display all the hues of a flower garden.

Burma is the home of the finest rubies, especially those having the exceedingly rare "pigeon's blood" color, a deep carmine slightly tinged with blue. Ruby of a paler color is found with excellent sapphire in the gem gravels of Ceylon. The Hills of Precious Stones is a district in Siam that has produced darker ruby and excellent sapphire for many generations. Siam alone yields over half of the world's supply of sapphire, though for a short time during the nineteenth century the province of Kashmir in India turned out blue sapphire superior to any others that have ever been known. The "electric blue" peculiar to Montana sapphire and the mystically beautiful star sapphire from Ceylon and elsewhere are also worthy of special mention.

**Emerald and Aquamarine, Another Mineral Family.** Emerald and aquamarine are both varieties of beryl, a mineral which also includes a pink gem called morganite and a golden gem called heliodor. These all occur in hard six-sided crystals that lend themselves ideally to being cut and set in jewelry. Ordinary opaque beryl is the chief source of metallic beryllium, which is an important alloy of copper.

Emerald, "green as a meadow in spring," has no equal

for color among the gems. The fabulous stones from Colombia—possessed by the Incas and despoiled by the Conquistadors—seem almost to have taken on the deep color of the dense jungle which guards the mines that produced them, mines purposely hidden from the invader, then swallowed up by the encroaching forest, and rediscovered by accident several hundred years later.

The name aquamarine means "sea water" and properly describes the pleasant color of this gem, a lovely blending of blue and green which varies like the changing moods of the sea. Some stones are pure blue, but most of them are greenish blue to bluish green, with one hue or the other predominating.

An infinitesimally small amount of the chromium oxide that gives emerald its incomparable color creates an enormous amount of value. Up to a certain limit, it may be worth more per ounce than almost anything else in the world; beyond that point, of course, additional coloring matter is undesirable, for it darkens the stone too much. The coloring agent in aquamarine is iron oxide. Whereas aquamarine has a notably perfect internal structure, emerald is nearly always flawed, so much so that imitation emeralds are deliberately made with flaws to resemble natural ones.

In spite of their fundamental similarity, emerald and aquamarine have a different geologic origin and so they are seldom found together. Besides the wonderful Colombian specimens, admirable smaller emeralds have come from the Ural Mountains in Siberia, which have likewise given us good aquamarines. Brazil is the chief source of aquamarine, credited with crystals of prodigious size, while Ceylon and Madagascar are other leading producers.

**Cat's-Eye.** One of the most fascinating of gems is cat's-eye. Its mysterious band of light glides furtively over the rounded surface of the stone as it is turned from side to side. This shifting light is called chatoyancy and is caused by the reflection of light from tiny hollow canals, numbering as many as 65,000 to the inch. The effect is best shown when the gem is shaped somewhat like a coffee bean.

The true cat's-eye is a variety of chrysoberyl, the third hardest of all minerals. It should not be confused with quartz cat's-eye, which is a common and inferior substitute, nor with the "Chinese cat's-eye" shell brought back in quantity from South Pacific islands during the Second World War.

Chrysoberyl cat's-eye comes in a range of colors with contrasting bands. Honey yellow, apple green, and dark green are the most valuable background colors. Most cat's-eye is recovered in Ceylon, where the natives regard it as a potent charm against evil spirits.

**Opal.** "Opal shows the most glorious colors to be seen in the world, save only those of clouds," wrote John Ruskin, expressing the feelings of everyone who has thrilled to the evanescent play of colors that rise from the depths of this gem, darting from spot to spot, hiding as the stone is moved and appearing again at another angle, unexpectedly and more beautiful than before. Nowhere are there hues of greater purity, the red redder or the green greener or the orange more flaming.

Opal of ancient times, known as Hungarian opal, came from Mármaros in the Nagy-Bánya district of what is now Czechoslovakia. The colors scintillate on a white or pale-tinted background, and so this variety, which is also found in several places in Australia and in Honduras, is called white opal.

In startling contrast to it is the black opal of Australia and Nevada. Against a curtain of dark blue, gray, or black the opal colors flash in incomparable richness, glowing like a "smothered mass of hidden fire."

The colors of opal seem to be due to the interference of light (as in soap bubbles) from layers in the stone that vary slightly in water content from one another. This difference has resulted from the way in which the original jellylike opal substance was deposited from natural hot springs or

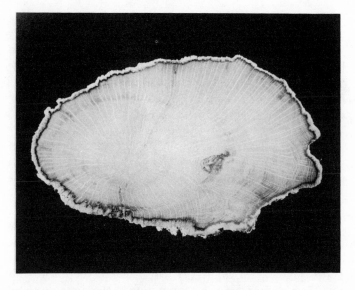

Fig. 22—Opalized wood, sectioned to show the original rays and bark now turned to opal. Clover Creek, Idaho. (*Courtesy of Ward's Natural Science Establishment.*)

other hot waters, then cooled, hardened, and cracked, the openings eventually becoming filled with new deposits of opal having an unequal amount of water.

An interesting feature of the black opal from Nevada and Australia is that it is found replacing fossil wood, shells of sea animals, and bones of extinct reptiles which lived in the former days when dinosaurs ruled the earth. Most opal occurs in thin seams in the rock.

**Tourmaline, the Rainbow Gem.** One of the most striking members of the mineral kingdom is tourmaline, a gem unsurpassed in its diversity of color, a mineral of curious properties and exciting history.

Its chemical composition is exceedingly complex, seeming to have incorporated "a little of everything," as John Ruskin put it, becoming "more like a medieval doctor's prescription than the making of a respectable mineral."

Although a mineral that must have been tourmaline was known in ancient times, it was lost sight of until centuries later, when its peculiar ability to attract ashes and straws in the hot sun was noted by some Dutch children. This strange property, described further in Chapter 3, is not the only noteworthy feature of tourmaline. Most certainly the unexcelled array of colors is the real reason for the increasing popularity that tourmaline has enjoyed during the past three hundred years. Not only does it appear in almost every imaginable hue, in or out of the rainbow, but the colors occur in combination. Thus a single crystal may be half green and half red; or green, white, and red, striped like a candy cane or zoned like a watermelon. Colorless crystals may be capped by a black top, and many other combinations are recorded.

American tourmaline has been mined principally in Maine and California. Brazil, Russia, Siberia, Madagascar, and the island of Elba rank as the most prolific foreign producers.

**Garnet.** The unpopularity of the familiar brown garnet, distracting attention from the merits of the other colors of garnet, has lifted somewhat, as garnet has crept slowly back into acceptance. Well it might, because in addition to the Bohemian garnet so dear to Victorian ladies, the garnet group includes a substantial range of minerals occurring in several agreeable colors.

Pyrope garnet is the common brown garnet referred to above. Almandite garnet at its best has a deep, clear red color, usually tinged with violet. Rhodolite garnet preserves the delicate hue of roses and rhododendrons. Grossularite garnet offers pink, orange, jade-, gooseberry-, and cinnamon-colored varieties. There is even a brilliant green garnet, called demantoid, which often substitutes for emeralds in diamond-set rings.

**Zircon, Gem of Mystery.** Long shrouded in obscurity, even as to its history and the origin of its name, zircon has yielded many of its fundamental secrets during the past twenty years. Its scientific properties make zircon one of the most extraordinary of gems.

Although showy red and green zircons are known, three other colors represent the majority of zircons seen in jewelry. The rich golden-brown gems are approached for magnificence by no other stones of that color. The unique blue zircon has attained world-wide popularity within a comparatively short while. Most familiar of all is the colorless zircon, so full of life and fire that in artificial light it is sometimes mistaken for diamond; it is often called "Matura diamond" because of its abundance in Matara, Ceylon.

These three varieties of zircon are occasionally found in nature, but most of the gems that are sold have been colored by artificial treatment involving the application of heat, either in air or in the absence of air, each method resulting in a different group of colors. A zircon industry, from mining to treatment to cutting, is concentrated in the region of Indo-China and Siam. Ceylon, the "Isle of Gems," is the other major source of supply.

**Topaz.** The name topaz arouses vision of a typically yellow gem. Yet all topaz is not yellow, nor are all yellow stones topaz, as is widely believed. Perhaps the loveliest hue of topaz is blue; light green is another attractive color. Though red topaz is extremely scarce, charming rose and pink stones are produced by the clever application of heat to brownish specimens.

Characterized by a remarkably slick surface, topaz has an odd slippery feeling that distinguishes it from other minerals. It ranks fourth in hardness among precious stones. Some huge, clear, well-formed crystals of topaz, weighing up to 600 pounds each, have been acquired from Brazil in recent years. The quality of Russian and Siberian topaz is unmatched. Ceylon is another place holding an enviable reputation in the market, though still other countries also produce good material.

**Turquoise.** The demand for turquoise has reached new heights, owing to the present vogue for American jewelry of Western design. Turquoise has long been admired greatly by the Indians, especially the Navajos, who have treasured it more than anything else in their possession. They mined it long before the arrival of the white man. The extensive deposits of Los Cerrillos, in New Mexico, were the most important; since their exhaustion they have been succeeded by mines in various localities in the states of Nevada, Colorado, and Arizona.

Earlier than the New Mexican deposits, the finest of all turquoise was produced near Nishapur in Iran; Persian turquoise is still the standard of quality. The ancient turquoise from the Sinai Peninsula, which found its way into Egyptian jewelry, is even older. The inhabitants of lofty Tibet today buy turquoise to wear with coral; the two gems present a colorful contrast.

Crystals of turquoise have been found only in Virginia. Everywhere else the mineral occurs in nuggets or veins in broken rock. Streaks of clay and iron oxide crisscrossing the stone are called its matrix and are taken as evidence of genuineness.

**Jade.** Jade comprises two different minerals so similar in appearance that the Chinese, to whom jade was the noblest of gems, did not distinguish between them. Jadeite is now regarded as the more valuable of the two because it has a richer look and comes in more colors. Nephrite is less translucent and considerably more abundant.

Superior toughness is the most characteristic physical property of jade. The structure is so intimately intergrown that it resists almost all attempts to break it. The Chinese artisans who have carved intricate and beautiful objects from jade deserve the highest praise for their skill and endless patience. A delightful property of jade is its resonance, so that slabs give forth pleasant sounds when struck.

Pure jade is white, but enough impurities are usually present to make jade yellow, blue, the familiar green, or almost any color. Most pieces are mottled.

Jadeite is virtually confined to Upper Burma, reaching

**Rocks and Minerals**

China only as an imported substance. Nephrite, on the other hand, is found in abundance in Turkestan, Siberia, New Zealand, Alaska, and Wyoming.

**Quartz Family.** Quartz, the commonest of minerals, includes a greater variety of gems than any other. Besides numerous industrially useful stones, quartz boasts handsome material of practically all colors and patterns. Most of the mineral specimens collected by hobbyists and cut by lapidaries, amateur or professional, are some sort of quartz.

Rock crystal, beloved of crystal gazers and familiar in bead necklaces, is clear quartz without any color. Amethyst, the most valuable quartz gem, contains a patchy distribution of iron sufficient to color it anywhere from a delicate orchid to a regal purple not seen elsewhere in the entire realm of gems. Rose quartz is a translucent stone of pink or rose-red hue which is caused by the presence of manga-

Fig. 23—Orbicular jasper from Santa Clara County, California, spotted with inclusions of contrasting color. (*Courtesy of Ward's Natural Science Establishment.*)

nese. Smoky quartz is a black stone which turns hazy brown as the light comes through; this distinctive color is ascribed to the effect of radium-bearing rocks, with which it is so generally associated. Tiger's-eye is derived from an asbestos mineral called crocidolite, which has been oxidized to golden brown from its original blue color and has been completely replaced by quartz; this inimitable gem, widely used in men's cameos, shows rippling bands of light which shift glossily across the surface when it is moved.

Certain kinds of quartz having an especially close-grained texture are grouped under the term chalcedony, which is considered by some mineralogists as a separate mineral. These gems are mainly opaque stones occurring in solid and mixed colors; they are appreciated for their individual designs and strange markings. Names such as agate, onyx, jasper, bloodstone, sardonyx, carnelian, and petrified wood refer to some of the literally countless varieties of chalcedony quartz.

# 9

# Pegmatite—Home of the Giant Minerals

Here is the Happy Hunting Ground for the mineral collector. Notable for the enormous size of their valuable crystals, as well as for their content of rare minerals of lesser dimensions, pegmatites hold the position of Lord High Treasurer in the mineral kingdom. They have no equal as natural storehouses of both of these unusual types of minerals.

Although the outstanding aspect of pegmatites is indeed their huge crystals, their more characteristic features are a variable grain-size and the striking intergrowths of microcline feldspar and quartz known as graphic granite. This distinctive rock, peculiar to pegmatites, gave them their name, for the term pegmatite is derived from a Greek word meaning "something fastened together." The two minerals interlock in an angular pattern that curiously resembles the cuneiform writing of ancient peoples. Runite, another name for graphic granite, likewise refers to this appearance of primitive writing due to the presence of fluted quartz rods in a matrix of microcline feldspar. Even though the percentages of both minerals are remarkably constant, there seems to be no definite orientation of either one. Graphic granite is an attractive and unique rock found in large quantities in areas of pegmatite.

The irregularity of grain size in pegmatite is also worthy of attention. Individual crystals range from a fraction of an inch to the colossal sizes of the feldspar and spodumene described on page 107. The size may change within short distances in the same deposit. The mineral composition, width, and position also may vary markedly all along the length of each pegmatite body.

Pegmatites are related to the deeply formed igneous rocks. Although they may have any composition and no two of them are quite alike, the majority belong to the granite group of rocks—so much so that unless stated otherwise the term pegmatite is taken to mean granite pegmatite.

Ordinary pegmatites consist chiefly of great masses of quartz and microcline feldspar, the dominant minerals in granite. Some contain booklike segregations of muscovite or biotite mica, perhaps feet or yards in diameter. Albite, a member of the plagioclase feldspar series, may be abundant, often in a tabular or platy form called cleavelandite.

It is when the less common minerals, many of them not known elsewhere, begin to appear that pegmatite presents

Fig. 24—The crystal of beryl was broken and later cemented by the milky quartz. North Groton, New Hampshire. (*Courtesy of Ward's Natural Science Establishment.*)

its full quota of gargantuan crystals. Beryl, topaz, and tour-maline are among the most likely of these, but the list is extensive. While not all of these minerals are of conspicuous size, enough of them do occur to uphold the reputation of pegmatite. Not long ago a mine in Madagascar yielded a single crystal of beryl weighing nearly 40 tons, surpassing even the 18- to 27-foot monsters previously obtained from New England and the Black Hills. Among the mammoth crystals of blue and colorless topaz brought from Minas Geraes, Brazil, in recent years have been some weighing as much as 600 pounds each, yet well formed and clear throughout. At the Bob Ingersoll mine near Keystone, South Dakota, was found a columbite crystal which weighed about a ton. A milky white crystal of quartz, having an estimated weight of 13 tons, was found about 1951 in a mine in the Balkhash Steppe in Siberia, where large quartz crystals are not too rare in the weathered granite. A more complete enumeration of record-breaking products of pegmatite crys-tallization, if compiled, would make interesting reading.

Among the pegmatites related to the basic rocks, in which quartz is scarce or absent, are those characterized by horn-blende and plagioclase feldspar. Phlogopite mica and apa-tite are other prominent constituents. Phlogopite from a crystal weighing almost 7 tons was taken from the Purdy mine at Eau Clair, Ontario, and apatite crystals from Buck-ingham Township, Ottawa County, Quebec, have exceeded 6 feet in circumference and 550 pounds in weight.

The wartime search for strategic and critical minerals led to more detailed studies of pegmatites than had been made before. These investigations emphasized the existence of dis-tinct zones, each of which may have its own typical minerals. Thus, although the complexities are many and gradational boundaries are more frequent than sharp contacts, recogni-zable units include border zones, wall zones, intermediate zones, and cores. This information increases the amount of recoverable minerals and reduces operating expenses.

During the Second World War pegmatites were examined

from Maine to California in the unrelenting search for beryl (used as a copper alloy and later in the atomic bomb), tantalum minerals (for vacuum tubes), quartz crystals (for frequency control in electronics), muscovite (for electrical insulation), and lithium minerals (for red flares and other uses). Pegmatites also contain rare-earth and radioactive minerals. The chief peacetime mineral recovered from pegmatites is microcline feldspar for the ceramic industry. Tin (as cassiterite), kaolin of pottery grade, and numerous gems are also obtained commercially from this kind of rock.

A pegmatite is probably the last part of the body of molten rock (called magma) to solidify, retaining until the end considerable amounts of steam and other vapors. The gases help to lower the temperature at which the molten matter hardens, thereby giving the minerals in it a longer time to grow into their fantastic dimensions.

As magma becomes solid it shrinks and cracks develop, in which the remaining liquid will collect, so that pegmatites occupy fissures within the parent body. These openings are often shaped like caverns and are known as miarolitic cavities, occasionally allowing room enough for a man to stand upright in them. "Pockets" of this sort have furnished tons of superb crystals, either projecting inward or "frozen." Other pegmatite solutions move into fractures in adjacent rock, sometimes apparently to a considerable distance from their source; metamorphic rocks next to vast bodies of granite are a favored home for such pegmatites.

There is little doubt that many of the most interesting pegmatites are the result of later solutions acting upon the original deposit and changing it, producing a secondary pegmatite, though the relative importance of this replacement process is uncertain. Lithium minerals such as lepidolite, the pink mica, and rubellite, the pink tourmaline, are especially noteworthy in this type of pegmatite, as at Pala, California, and in the Black Hills. Beryl and albite feldspar are other important minerals formed in this way.

In pegmatites are found extraordinary concentrations of

certain rare elements as characteristic minerals. Some of these minerals are familiar enough in granite and related rocks but always in small grains that usually require a microscope to detect. Tourmaline, zircon, fluorite, apatite, and monazite are examples of them. In pegmatites, however, they may appear in substantial sizes, as witness the 58-pound crystal of monazite from North Carolina, the 15-pound zircon crystal from Brudenell Township in Ontario, and the quarter-ton crystals of apatite already mentioned from Buckingham Township in Quebec.

The availability of rare elements and the slow and presumably carefully protected conditions within a pegmatite contribute to the forming of clear and excellently shaped crystals of gem minerals renowned for their purity and beauty. Many of the gems described in Chapter 8 have their home in pegmatites.

The bodies of pegmatite themselves are usually tabular or somewhat lens-shaped, though they have been determined to have almost any outline, often existing as massive blobs within the parent rock. In length they range from a few inches to a few hundred yards, exceptional ones being several miles long.

Although pegmatites are widely distributed over the globe, some areas are especially famous for them. In size and profusion, perhaps the most spectacular localities in the United States are some in New England, especially in Maine and Connecticut; Amelia, Virginia; western North Carolina; South Dakota, in the Black Hills; central Colorado; north-central New Mexico; Latah County, Idaho; and Pala, California. A once-prolific locality was Barringer Hill, Texas, now drowned by the Buchanan Reservoir. Canada contains a great many pegmatites in Ontario and Quebec. Norway and Sweden include superior deposits. The pegmatites of Madagascar, South Africa, and Brazil are likewise of first-rate interest. The Alps, Pyrenees, Urals, Andes, and other towering mountain ranges are the home of pegmatites in abundance.

# 10

# Atomic Minerals

The universal interest in sources of atomic energy is at its height. Atomic minerals now represent the raw material of future undreamed-of prosperity or else disaster beyond imagination. Radioactive minerals have become the most urgently critical of all geologic products.

Beginning with the simplest element, hydrogen, the atoms are successively heavier and more complex, each having one more negatively charged electron than the atom before it, and one more positively charged proton. Eventually the structure becomes so unstable that it can no longer hold together; such an atom then explodes, ejecting parts of itself as radiation, and settles back again as a simpler, lighter, and more stable atom. Sir William Ramsay expressed it this way:

> So the atoms in turn, we now clearly discern,
> Fly to bits with the utmost facility;
> They wend on their way, and in splitting, display
> An absolute lack of stability.

This point is reached with the atoms heavier than lead, which has 82 electrons and 82 protons, and is the largest of the entirely stable elements.

The spontaneous emission of energy generated in this way is called radioactivity, which cannot be seen, heard, or felt, but can be detected by means of an instrument such as a Geiger counter or by one of the special methods described later. The radiation is composed of three different kinds, which are either extremely tiny particles or waves, to which the terms alpha $(\alpha)$, beta $(\beta)$, and gamma $(\gamma)$ radiation are applied.

Alpha radiation actually consists of atoms of helium which have lost their two electrons, so that they now carry only the positive charge of the nucleus that is left. These particles travel at speeds so high that they break up most of the atoms lying directly in their paths and so spend their force within a few inches of air; they can be stopped by thin sheets of paper. Beta radiation consists of electrons or particles having a negative charge; traveling with wavelike motion almost as fast as light but shattering only a small percentage of the atoms they hit, they are somewhat more penetrating than alpha particles and can go through a foot or so of air or a thin sheet of lead before being destroyed. They will darken a photographic plate and can be bent out of their straight paths by a magnet; this is the principle whereby the cyclotron is utilized for producing neutrons to treat cancer. Gamma radiation consists of true rays, which are like those of X-rays and light, and so are not electrically charged, but they are a million times shorter in wave length than ordinary visible light. They readily pass through at least three inches of lead and they darken photographic film, as well as showing other interesting effects. In addition to these three kinds of atomic radiation, heat energy is also given off, together with the very light gas helium.

Atomic energy as spoken of today is really nuclear energy, for it is derived from the nucleus, which contains practically all the mass and energy of the atom. The great speed with which the nuclear particles and radiation travel is the source of their energy. When bombarded by neutrons, which are uncharged particles within the nucleus, heavy radioactive atoms (such as uranium) undergo fission and split into two fragments, liberating additional neutrons. These repeat the process when they encounter other heavy atoms, producing a chain reaction which perpetuates itself and soon releases a tremendous amount of energy. The complete fissioning of one pound of uranium-235 will release as much heat as

1,530 tons of coal, and within one-hundredth of a second, one cubic yard of powdered uranium oxide could supply enough force to lift a weight of a billion tons to a height of 13 miles!

Three series of natural radioactive elements are known, besides a few independent elements of similar nature. Each series begins with a heavy element—uranium-238, -235, or thorium—and ends with lead, which is not radioactive. In between are a number of radioactive elements, which replace one another in regular order at a rate that is not affected by heat, pressure, or any other known outside influence. One part of radium is present in a mineral for each 3,400,000 parts of uranium-238 when equilibrium is reached. The time required for half of a given amount of any of these elements to disintegrate into a different element is called its half life, which also means that half of the remainder will change in the next period of the same length, and so on. Uranium-238 has the enormously long half life of 4,500,000,000 years. At the other extreme, half of thorium C' (which is really polonium) disappears in only one ten-billionth of a second. Half of radium-226 goes in 1,590 years. Thus it is seen that no final disappearance of a radioactive substance ever occurs, for there is always a last half left, although ultimately it becomes very small indeed.

Elements that are chemically alike but have slightly different atomic weights are known as isotopes. Every element has a number of isotopes, some of which are stable and some radioactive, though the elements beyond bismuth (number 83) exist only in radioactive form. Radioactive isotopes of the common elements that are important in the life processes of plants and animals are proving of great value in medical research and the cure of disease. As "tracers" they have helped to make clear for the first time the mechanism of many bodily functions. Radioactive carbon is playing a major part in such investigations because it behaves almost exactly like stable natural carbon, yet its movements can be followed through living tissue and complex chemical reactions. The isotope of uranium, called U-235, was used to produce the atomic bomb. Another isotope, U-238, is employed in making the new heavy elements; plutonium, one of these, can also be used for weapons and "atomic" energy in general because, like U-235, it is capable of fission.

Radium is the most familiar of the radioactive elements because of its dramatic discovery by Pierre and Marie Curie and its early use in medicine. In the nuclear energy program, however, uranium and thorium are the most important elements. Uranium is the only one of present value, though the Atomic Energy Commission is not overlooking deposits of thorium minerals—of which monazite is the principal one—for possible future use. Radioactivity apparently due to potassium—which is an abundant element in many rocks and minerals, although it does not belong to any of the three series already mentioned—exists in many places, especially in the "Red Beds" of the western United States, though not in commercial concentrations.

There are over 100 different radioactive minerals, and about twice that many names have been applied to them. Some of the minerals are fairly common, while others are extremely rare. Many other radioactive minerals of uncertain value are also known to exist, but they have not yet been adequately studied. The amount of metal in the various uranium minerals ranges from a trace to more than 70 per cent.

## PRIMARY URANIUM MINERALS

Primary uranium minerals are those that were formed by hot solutions rising into the rocks from below and have not altered significantly since they were originally deposited. They are mostly black or dark brownish red, having a pitchy, shiny, or dull-metallic look, and they are noticeably heavy. Found mostly in metal-bearing veins and in the very coarse granitelike rock called pegmatite (see Chapter 9), these primary minerals may have a rusty iron crust and coatings of brightly colored secondary uranium minerals. Pitchblende and uraninite, the chief primary minerals of uranium, sometimes weather to a greenish cast, and may also show a powdery pink coating (due to cobalt) or a green coating (due to nickel).

**Pitchblende.** Its usual black color and pitchy luster gave pitchblende its name. This is the uranium oxide mineral, first mined at Joachimsthal in Bohemia, from which Madame Curie extracted the first radium, and it is the chief constituent in virtually all high-grade uranium ores. It occurs in veins in almost any kind of rock, together with ores of such metals as silver, copper, cobalt, nickel, iron, lead, and bismuth. The "big three" producing countries— Canada (on the eastern shore of Great Bear Lake in Northwest Territories), Czechoslovakia (in the Joachimsthal district), and the Republic of the Congo (in the province of Katanga) are the main sources of pitchblende. In the United States the richest pitchblende is in Colorado, especially near Central City.

Pitchblende is found in irregularly rounded lumps, which break with a conchoidal fracture. Its color is dark, generally black, sometimes showing a grayish or greenish tinge; almost never is it reddish brown or brownish black, as are many of the less-valuable primary uranium minerals. When crushed or powdered its streak is always black, perhaps with a grayish or greenish shade, but not in any way brownish. Sometimes instead of being pitchy, this mineral is dull and at other times it has a glossy surface. Occasionally it appears banded or slightly fibrous. Pitchblende is heavier than iron, having a specific gravity between 6.5 and 8.5, and has about the hardness (5 to 6) of a steel knife blade. Its composition varies considerably because of the impurities present, which may include rare earths, lead, helium, zirconium, and water.

**Uraninite.** Uraninite is generally regarded as a crystallized form of pitchblende. Hence it is heavier (8 to 10), and chemically purer, though it, too, is usually oxidized and

contains extraneous matter. It ordinarily occurs in octahedrons, cubes, and other isometric crystals, 1 to 3 inches
long. Otherwise its appearance and properties are very
similar to those of pitchblende. Although its uranium content is high, uraninite has not yet been discovered in profitable amounts except where closely associated with pitchblende. Its usual home, however, is in granite pegmatite,
where it occurs with large masses of quartz, feldspar, and
black mica. An interesting feature of such deposits is that
the radioactive energy may discolor the rock reddish brown
and crack it open for a distance of several yards.

The other primary uranium minerals—including such intriguing names as betafite, euxenite, and samarskite—also
occur mostly in pegmatite. They are found in groups of
black or dark brownish red crystals. The thin edges and
powder of these minerals have a reddish or brown color.
Davidite, coffinite, and brannerite have become of commercial value since 1951.

## SECONDARY URANIUM MINERALS

Secondary uranium minerals are those that have changed
from some previous primary mineral by weathering or other
means. They may have been carried in solution by ground
waters moving through the rocks. These minerals are recognized by their brilliant green, yellow, and orange colors,
often contrasting with the somber-looking primary minerals.
Such an attractive combination is seen at Grafton Center,
New Hampshire, and Mitchell County, North Carolina,
where orange gummite is found on yellow uranophane,
which in turn rests upon black uraninite. The secondary
uranium minerals occur in flat micalike plates, groups of
small crystals, and earthy or powdery masses, being found
in rock pores and cracks, where they frequently accompany
decaying vegetation, oil, peat, lignite coal, and fossil plants.

**Carnotite.** The main supply of uranium in the United
States comes from the unique deposits of secondary carno-

tite in the Colorado Plateaus. Blanketing a large area in the Four Corners region where Colorado, Utah, Arizona, and New Mexico meet at a common point are sedimentary rocks coated with yellow carnotite, associated with a micalike vanadium mineral called roscoelite, and other related minerals. Carnotite is a potassum uranium vanadate and has a history as varied as its composition. The ore was at first mined for its small amount of gold, but in 1899, three years after the discovery of radioactivity, its true composition became known; it was soon produced for radium and some uranium, with a minor by-product of vanadium for use as a steel alloy. The analysis was done in Paris and the mineral was named after a French engineer.

After the disclosure of the tremendously rich pitchblende deposits in the Belgian Congo, American carnotite went into a decline until revived solely as an ore of vanadium. Some uranium was extracted later for coloring glass and other miscellaneous purposes, and there the industry remained until the research leading up to the atomic bomb took place. Carnotite is one of the most vivid of all minerals; a little of its canary-yellow color will stain a good deal of rock. Low-quality specimens are likely to have a brown stain or greenish tinge. Most of the carnotite has an earthy look, but when well crystallized it has a pearly appearance. Radium trees! Uranium dinosaur bones! Radioactive oyster shells! These are fantastic sounding but true occurrences in the rugged Colorado Plateaus. Here the bright yellow carnotite is present as a powdery crust on sandstone and as a replacement of petrified and carbonized wood, dinosaur bones, and mollusk shells. Near the San Miguel River two petrified logs were "mined," yielding $175,000 in radium, $27,300 in uranium, and $28,200 in vanadium.

**Tyuyamunite.** As calcium substitutes for potassium, carnotite becomes the unmanageable mineral tyuyamunite. Named from a Siberian locality, it is widely distributed in the Colorado Plateaus, especially near Grants, New Mexico, at the Ambrosia Lake deposit.

**Torbernite, Autunite.** Torbernite and autunite, similar to each other, are uranium minerals of some economic importance. They occur in thin translucent plates and so are sometimes called uranium mica, though they have no connection with any of the true micas. Torbernite, a hydrous copper uranium phosphate, is bright green, whereas autunite, a hydrous calcium uranium phosphate, is light yellow or greenish yellow. Autunite is consistently fluorescent in a yellowish-green color.

The other secondary uranium minerals are secured mostly in the Republic of the Congo where the original rich veins of pitchblende have weathered deeply in the tropical climate.

## DETECTION OF RADIOACTIVITY

A number of efficient methods and instruments have been developed to detect and measure radioactivity.

**Radioautographs.** Radioactivity was discovered in 1896 by the French physicist Henri Becquerel, who found that a photographic plate, though wrapped in lightproof black paper, had become darkened by invisible radiation evidently coming from a uranium compound. This test still remains useful for radioactivity, especially now that such firms as Eastman Kodak Company produce photographic film that is unusually sensitive to such radiation but surprisingly resistant to ordinary light. A radioactive mineral will take its own picture, called a radioautograph, even with standard film. Simply put a key, coin, or other distinctively shaped metallic object on the wrapped film and then gently place a smooth surface of the rock or mineral specimen on top of it. An image of the piece of metal will show on the film after it is developed; the sharpness will depend upon the strength of the radioactivity in the mineral and the length of exposure, as well as upon the kind of film used.

**Electroscope.** The simple instrument called an electroscope, devised for recognizing infinitesimally small traces of matter, is a most sensitive piece of apparatus. It will betray

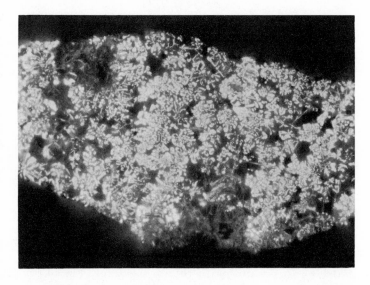

Fig. 25—This specimen of radioactive uraninite from New Hampshire has taken its own picture on photographic film in the dark. (*Courtesy of Ward's Natural Science Establishment.*)

the presence of a millionth of a gram of uranium, and even less of certain other elements. Electroscopes are sold for a few dollars by firms dealing in scientific instruments, or they can be made from such common articles as a glass bottle, a tin can, an aluminum foil of the kind used to decorate signs. An electroscope consists of a metal rod from which two pieces of very thin gold or aluminum leaf are loosely suspended. These leaves are enclosed in a glass container, or preferably a metal case with a glass window. Part of the metal rod extends outside the container but is separated from the case itself by passing through an insulating material such as plastic or sealing wax. The electroscope can be charged by stroking a glass or hard rubber rod on a piece of cloth and then holding it close to or against the top of the metal rod. The positive charges from the glass, or the negative charges from the rubber move down the metal rod to the leaves where, being of like kind, they repel each other, causing the leaves to fall together again when a radioactive mineral is brought near.

**Scintilliscope.** Another inexpensive instrument that can also be bought or made at home for the detection of radioactivity is called a scintilliscope, spintharoscope, or radioscope. It employs much the same principle as the luminous dials on watches and alarm clocks. Alpha particles from radioactive minerals, striking powdered zinc sulfide, cause the energy to be converted into visible light. Each tiny crystal struck by an alpha particle emits a single flash of light. Until magnified, these flashes merge together into a general glow or luminosity, but if you look at your watch dial through a hand lens you will see the individual sparks. The paint used in such dials is zinc sulfide powder mixed with a radioactive chemical which causes a steady bombardment of alpha particles during the life of the paint. The instrument mentioned here consists merely of a small tube with a screen of powdered zinc sulfide at one end and a magnifying glass in the eyepiece at the other end. The sample is carefully introduced between them so that it will not touch the powder, and its degree of activity can readily be observed in a dark room and might even be measured by counting.

**Uranium Bead Test.** These tests, and the Geiger counter described below, detect radioactivity but they do not distinguish between the different radioactive elements. Uranium, however, being at present the only one with a commercial value, the following easy test for uranium alone is worth knowing. First, one end of a piece of iron, nichrome, or platinum wire is bent into a small loop about one-quarter inch across. Within the loop is placed some sodium fluoride powder (obtainable from a chemical supply firm), which is then heated in the flame of an alcohol lamp or other hot burner until the powder melts into a small drop called a bead. The hot bead is then touched to a few grains of the powdered mineral to be tested, and it is heated again until the mineral melts into the bead. After cooling, the bead is viewed under ultraviolet light (see page 157). It will glow with a bright yellow-green color if uranium is present. This fluorescent bead test is usually a good one, although it does not work if much thorium (which is also radioactive) or the rare-earth elements (such as cerium) are present. Fluorescence of the original rock specimen itself is not, however, an adequate test, inasmuch as autunite is the only uranium mineral of any importance that can be relied upon to fluoresce in ultraviolet light.

**Geiger Counter.** Recording the rapid click-click that may spell fortune in this atomic age is the Geiger-Mueller counter, so sensitive that it can indicate the passage of a single electron or cosmic-ray particle. The basis of the Geiger counter, as it is now usually called, is the ability of radioactive emanations to enable gas to conduct electricity. This same property also permits the escape of electric charges from the leaves of an electroscope into the surrounding air, as already described. The original Geiger counter, consisting of a wire surrounded by a metal cylinder that was filled with low-pressure air, has been modified so that numerous types are available for various purposes. A difference of potential, or degree of electrification, is maintained between the wire and the cylinder, but it is slightly too small to permit a current to flow between them without some additional assistance. This help is supplied by the radioactive mineral and by cosmic rays always present in the atmosphere. The particles of radiation ionize the gas, that is, charge it electrically, producing electric current. This current comes in pulses which are amplified as a flashing light or a series of clicks in an earphone, or can be made to operate a meter.

Such technical progress has been made in a few years that portable Geiger counters are now available for outdoor use that operate from flashlight batteries, weigh less than one pound, and can be carried in a coat pocket as easily as a camera. Thousands of them are taken daily into the field by uranium prospectors. The tube itself is sometimes enclosed in a separate protective metal case so that it can be used as a probe to explore inside cracks in the rock.

Since cosmic rays from outside the earth also affect the Geiger counter, producing what is called the "background count," due allowance must be made for them. An average count for the normal cosmic radiation at a given time and place is determined before a count is taken for radioactivity, and it is then subtracted from the total. If the cosmic rays are blocked off in a deep hole, the count will go down. Instructions for use are furnished with most instruments that are sold.

**Scintillation Counter.** Substituting a crystal called a phosphor and a photomultiplier tube in place of a vacuum tube as its gamma-ray recording mechanism has produced the scintillation counter. This delicate instrument is considerably more expensive than a Geiger counter but it is making mineral history as it is being flown over barren wasteland to outline areas that may prove favorable for detailed ground prospecting. It is even being used in reverse— for in Africa the kimberlite pipes, which may be diamond-bearing, exhibit deficient radioactivity compared with the surrounding rocks, and they are consequently being discovered through aerial surveys.

**Berylometer.** Related in principle to the scintillation counter, the berylometer is a portable (though heavy and expensive) instrument that detects unfailingly the presence of the metallic element beryllium in any mineral. The device contains radioactive antimony-124, which produces gamma rays; these convert ordinary beryllium into a lighter isotope, releasing neutrons, which are counted by a scintillator.

# 11

# Minerals That Glow in the Dark

Certain quite ordinary-looking minerals suddenly become a fairyland of strikingly brilliant colors when they are exposed to ultraviolet rays. These rays are entirely invisible, but the minerals transform them into colors that can be seen by the human eye. Sometimes the weird effect persists even after the ultraviolet rays have been turned off.

In 1602 an Italian shoemaker, who practiced alchemy in his spare time, noticed that some specimens of barite which he had collected shone in the dark after they had previously been in strong sunlight or in front of a fire. He believed that the barite was storing up light and then giving it off again. Others realized that, inasmuch as the color of the light was being changed during the process, there must be another reason.

When Sir Isaac Newton passed a beam of sunlight through a glass prism, which he is said to have bought for a penny at historic Stourbridge Fair, he obtained a sequence of rainbow colors called the spectrum. From this experiment he proved that white light is really a perfect blending of the rays that separately are colored red, orange, yellow, green, blue, and violet. (The color indigo comes between blue and violet but most people cannot see it.) Each color of the spectrum, and every intermediate hue, is a ray of different wave length or frequency. In Fig. 26 the distance from A to C is one wave length; so is the distance between B and D. The frequency is the number of wave lengths which will pass a given point in one second of time. The shorter the wave length, the higher the frequency, since the shorter rays can vibrate more rapidly in the same time interval.

Visible light, however, is only a tiny part of the vast range of electromagnetic radiation which constitutes the "universe of light." At one end of the region of visible colored light are found the heat (infrared) rays, while at the other end are situated the ultraviolet rays, which are those chiefly responsible for luminescence. Radiation beyond the infrared includes microwaves and other waves which are of still longer wave lengths than red light; beyond the ultraviolet

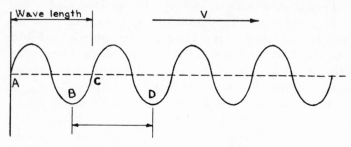

Fig. 26—Curve of light, showing wave length.

are X-rays, gamma rays, and cosmic rays. If the visible spectrum from red to violet were represented by a yardstick, the entire radiation, most of it invisible, would reach over 5,000,-000 miles!

When expressed in angstrom units (A.U.) —each of which is one hundred-millionth of a centimeter (about 254 million to an inch) —the ultraviolet ranges between 1,600 and 3,800 A.U., whereas the visible spectrum extends from 3,800 to 8,000 A.U.

## LUMINESCENCE

Ultraviolet radiation is often called cold light because it is accompanied by only a small amount of heat energy, which is a welcome feature of the *fluorescent* tubes so popular for modern illumination. It is also called black light because it is invisible. Though not itself visible, it can be converted into visible colors by fluorescent substances. Those that continue to glow after the source of radiation is removed are referred to as *phosphorescent*. Both of these phenomena are termed luminescence.

Luminescence can be produced by other radiation besides ultraviolet. Exposure to X-rays, cathode rays, and radioactivity will sometimes give an even stronger glow, but their use is limited by matters of inconvenience, expense, and danger. The commercial development of good sources of ultraviolet radiation has made it the most practicable means of observing fluorescence and phosphorescence.

In each of these instances, however, shorter (invisible) wave lengths are changed into longer (visible) ones, a generalization known as Stokes' law and applicable in most cases. Sometimes short wave lengths of visible light, such as blue, can bring out longer wave lengths, say orange, but this effect is not commonly observed. Stokes' law is generally true owing to the fact that the shorter the wave length of the radiation, the more energy it is endowed with.

As the rays strike the atoms of luminescent minerals they displace electrons from their normal positions to paths farther out. The return of the electrons from these higher energy bands to their original orbits is accompanied by a release in the form of light of part of the newly acquired energy. Sir George G. Stokes named this effect fluorescence after the mineral fluorite, which often shows it.

The kind of phosphorescence that results when the electrons return slowly and the glow fades gradually is different from the phosphorescence that is due to biochemical reactions. Such an emission of light usually results from a slow burning or oxidation of organisms, as seen on the surface of the ocean, in decaying wood, in yellow phosphorus (whence its name), and perhaps in the light of fireflies and glow-worms. The type of phosphorescence in minerals, however, like fluorescence, requires that energy must first be absorbed by some mechanical means. Impurities seem to have a profound effect on the kind and degree of luminescence. Those that cause luminescence are called activators—among the best are manganese, copper, silver, lead, and uranium—whereas those that prevent it are called inhibitors.

Some minerals show other kinds of luminescence. These may be produced by heat, friction, crystallization, cooling, and electrochemical action. The glow obtained by heating is called *thermoluminescence;* diamond and fluorite (especially the chlorophane variety which emits a green glow) are among the minerals that react best. Light obtained by rubbing a mineral is called *triboluminescence.* It is shown by specimens of sphalerite from Chihuahua, Mexico, and Tsumeb in South-West Africa, which give off sparks when lightly tapped with a hammer in the dark. Three hundred years ago the Irish chemist Robert Boyle performed some novel experiments with triboluminescent diamonds.

**Fluorite.** Rare-earth elements are credited with causing luminescence in fluorite. A more appropriate mineral could better have been chosen to give its name to the phenomenon, because only a little fluorite responds to ultraviolet radiation. The color then is usually blue violet. Fluorite is an interesting mineral from other standpoints, however. It is a calcium fluoride of considerable industrial importance, serving as the source of hydrofluoric acid and as an indispensable flux in steelmaking. The massive material is usually spoken of as fluorspar. Beautiful single and twin crystals, belonging to the isometric system, occur in almost any color or in several multicolored combinations. The compact violet and purple fluorite, called blue john, from Derbyshire, England, was formerly much in demand for vases and other ornamental objects.

**Franklin Minerals.** The prosperous fluorescent light industry of today had its humble origin in the mines of the New Jersey Zinc Company at Franklin, New Jersey. Miners observed by accident that willemite, a zinc mineral, could be distinguished from the other ore minerals by the bright green glow that it gave when exposed in the dark to the ultraviolet spark from an iron-arc lamp. The research that was undertaken to devise improved methods of bringing about this distinguishing characteristic, in order to separate willemite from the rest of the ore, led to the invention of our present-day illumination. This Franklin ore is especially beautiful. In ordinary light the willemite, a zinc silicate, is apple green; its most typical associates are red zincite, which is zinc oxide; black franklinite, an oxide of zinc, iron, and manganese; and white calcite. Under ultraviolet light the willemite fluoresces green and the calcite glows with a rich watermelon red. Both of these contrasting colors are due to traces of manganese; pure willemite and calcite from other localities do not show this effect at all. The Franklin minerals also often phosphoresce in the same vivid hues. Two new minerals, barylite and calcium larsenite, were first discovered at Franklin because of their fluorescence; and two other minerals, wollastonite and pectolite, though previously known elsewhere, were recognized here for the same reason.

**Scheelite.** Scheelite, calcium tungstate, is one of the few minerals that always fluoresces, no matter where it is found. Being the most important tungsten mineral in North America, it was widely prospected for at night with ultraviolet lamps during the Second World War. The use of tungsten wire in the common light bulb has long been known, but the military need for this strategic metal is as a steel alloy; high-speed tool steels, for example, require tungsten to give them resistance to heat. Although it looks a good deal like white quartz, scheelite is remarkably heavy for a nonmetallic mineral and it can be distinguished by its blue fluorescence. This color tends toward yellow as the tungsten is replaced by molybdenum and the mineral becomes powellite.

**Scapolite.** The tawny yellow glow of scapolite from Ontario and Quebec is one of the most appealing colors among fluorescent minerals. Scapolite is a complex silicate sometimes called wernerite. Typical crystals of it are large and square, tapering bluntly above and below.

**Diamond.** Fluorescent diamonds, once thought to be rare, have lately come to be recognized as actually more abundant than the nonluminescent stones. Sky blue and cornflower blue are the most typical colors of South African diamonds. Diamonds that fluoresce conspicuously in daylight are more apt than others to reveal phosphorescence.

**Opal.** Mineral collectors in the western states are familiar with fluorescent opal from Nevada, Wyoming, and elsewhere. The cause of the color, mostly green, has been shown to be a small amount of a uranium compound.

**Hackmannite.** Only one mineral is known that undergoes an actual change of color as a result of exposure to ultraviolet light. This is hackmannite, a member of the feldspathoid group of silicates. White specimens from near Bancroft, Ontario, assume in spots a delicate pink hue when they are held in front of ultraviolet radiation, clearing again in sunlight. This curious reversible change takes place in the opposite way when freshly broken pink hackmannite loses its color in direct sunshine, gradually gaining it back in the dark. Other hackmannite from the same locality acquires in the sun a deep violet shade, which can be made to disappear rapidly with the aid of an ordinary electric-light bulb. The original discovery of this kind was reported on sodalite from Greenland.

## USES OF LUMINESCENCE

The value of luminescence for identifying gems, minerals, and ores is apparent. The fact that most of the effect is due to impurities is a disadvantage for this purpose, because two minerals of the same species but from different localities may fluoresce quite differently. It is an advantage, however, in recognizing the origin of certain minerals, as some of the fluorescent colors are distinctive for particular localities. The discovery and recovery of scheelite and willemite, important ores of tungsten and zinc, respectively, have been facilitated by their fluorescence, as is also true of the commercial minerals hydrozincite and zircon. A fluorescent screen is used in testing rocks for mercury.

Ultraviolet light has numerous valuable applications outside of the field of minerals. The television screen depends upon the principle of luminescence. Spectacular theatrical effects are obtained by using fluorescent dyes on the stage. Scientific criminology owes much to the use of fluorescence in recognizing and tracing fingerprints, fraudulent signatures and documents, and laundry marks. New medical uses for fluorescence are continually being learned; recent advances have combined radioactivity and fluorescence in the form of radioactive dyes which have an inexplicable affinity for tumor tissue, the exact location of which is then indicated by a Geiger counter.

Sunlight is rich in ultraviolet rays. Much of the beauty of rubies and of many diamonds is due to their fluorescence in daylight added to their natural color. Stokes employed lightning in some of his studies of fluorescence, but this method seems extreme for ordinary mineral work. For general purposes the modern types of ultraviolet light are recommended.

## ULTRAVIOLET LAMPS

Although, as previously said, the ultraviolet wave lengths cover only a tiny fraction of the electromagnetic series, they nevertheless extend over a wider range than any artificial source of illumination. To secure all available fluorescence more than one lamp is needed, for minerals vary in their reaction to different radiation. Standard equipment is made for either "long" wave lengths (with maximum concentration near 3,650 A.U.) or "short" wave lengths (concentrated near 2,537 A.U.), the latter being more desirable for the majority of specimens.

Another point to be emphasized is that any of the lamps will transmit some visible light which conceals the fluorescence. A proper filter must be added to eliminate as much as possible of the ordinary colors, usually purple.

Some of the equipment being manufactured today approaches the ideal fluorescent lamp—giving a wide range of ultraviolet radiation, uniform but intense illumination, and freedom from excessive heat and unpleasant fumes, while capable of being enclosed for protection, and portable for outdoor use.

One or more argon bulbs are satisfactory for inexpensive home use. These are similar in principle to the usual neon sign except that they are filled instead with argon mixed with other gases. They can be used without a filter and are screwed into any household electrical outlet. Willemite and wernerite are among the minerals that show up handsomely under the long wave lengths of the argon bulb.

The most suitable ultraviolet equipment is a mercury vapor lamp. This, too, is used in signs as well as in street lighting, furnishing the bright violet color of incandescent mercury gas. When fitted with an appropriate filter the new germicidal lamps, which are of this type, are excellent for our purpose.

SERPENTINE ASBESTOS;
Thetford, Quebec.

ANALCIME (twinned crys-
tals); Houghton County,
Michigan.

NATIVE COPPER; Houghton
County, Michigan.

PETRIFIED WOOD; near
Holbrook, Arizona.

ARAGONITE AND SULFUR;
Cianciana, Sicily.

AMBER; Baltic Sea Coast,
Germany.

*(Photos by Katherine H. Jensen, courtesy
of Ward's Natural Science Establishment.)*

SEMIOPAL; Nevada.

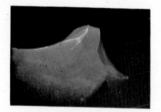

FLUORESCENT SEMIOPAL.

FLUORESCENT SCHEELITE; fluorescence contrasts with the darker matrix.

(*Courtesy of Ultra-Violet Products, Inc.*)

CALCITE CRYSTAL
ON DOLOMITE;
Penfield, New York.

*(Photo by Katherine H. Jensen, courtesy
of Ward's Natural Science Establishment.)*

TUNGSTEN ORE; normal white light does not show mineralization.

*(Courtesy of Ultra-Violet Products, Inc.)*

FLUORESCENT CALCITE; Bis-
bee, Arizona.

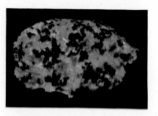

FLUORESCENT CALCITE.

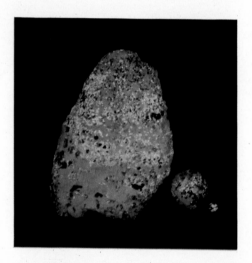

FLUORESCENT CALCITE AND WILLEMITE,
WITH BLACK FRANKLINITE;
Franklin, New Jersey.

*(Courtesy of Ultra-Violet Products, Inc.)*

CHALCEDONY GEODE (Chalcedony psuedomorph after Coral); Tampa Bay, Florida.

ARAGONITE (pisolitic); Eisenerz, Styria.

QUARTZ, variety Chalcedony (botryoidal); Emery County, Utah.

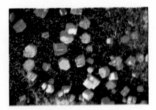

VANADINITE; near Tucson, Arizona.

OBSIDIAN (brown and black, shows conchoidal fracture); Lake County, Oregon.

WULFENITE; Chihuahua, Mexico.

*(Photos by Katherine H. Jensen, courtesy of Ward's Natural Science Establishment.)*

RICHLY FLUORESCENT MINERALS;
world-wide localities.

FLUORESCENT SCHEELITE;
Sinaloa, Mexico.

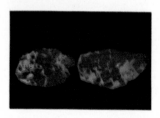

FLUORESCENT WILLEMITE
AND CALCITE; Franklin, New
Jersey.

*(Courtesy of Ultra-Violet Products, Inc.)*

FLUORESCENT MINERALS appear very ordinary in white light.

*(Courtesy of Ultra-Violet Products, Inc.)*

SCHEELITE; Nevada.

STILBITE; Paterson, New Jersey.

BARITE; Bad Lands, South Dakota.

QUARTZ, variety Rock Crystal; near Hot Springs, Arkansas.

QUARTZ, variety Milky Quartz; Ouray, Colorado.

ANDALUSITE, variety Chiastolite (crystal sections); Madera County, California.

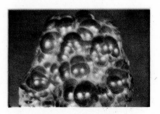

GOETHITE (mammillary); Ishpeming, Michigan.

(*Photos by Katherine H. Jensen, courtesy of Ward's Natural Science Establishment.*)

VARISCITE; near Fairfield, Utah.

TOURMALINE, variety Rubellite, in Lepidolite; San Diego, California.

*(Photos by Katherine H. Jensen, courtesy of Ward's Natural Science Establishment.)*

"SPHERES."

*(Courtesy of Ultra-Violet Products, Inc.)*

MINERALS IN ULTRA-VIOLET LIGHT; a rainbow of brilliant colors.

*(Courtesy of Ultra-Violet Products, Inc.)*

**COLLECTOR'S CABINET;** blue, white, and cream fluorescent minerals are scheelite, an ore of tungsten.

*(Courtesy of Ultra-Violet Products, Inc.)*

# 12

# Stones from the Sky

Although Thomas Jefferson was an enthusiastic and enlightened naturalist, he replied to a report that a shower of meteorites had been observed in New England by saying, "I could more easily believe that two Yankee professors would lie than that stones would fall from heaven!"

Yet it is now estimated that billions of individual meteorites enter the earth's atmosphere each day, of which 24 million can be seen or photographed by the incandescent trail that they leave. Indeed, however, only a few of that enormous number survive the devastating speed with which they travel.

Whereas a meteorite is solid matter from celestial space, a meteor or "shooting star" is only the flash of light caused by the rapid passage of a meteorite through the protective zone of the earth's atmosphere. There it burns violently enough to fuse, catch fire, and glow weirdly as the burning portion is stripped away. A bolide or fireball is a meteor that appears at least as bright as Jupiter or Venus, and some meteors have been described to be as large as the full moon; the solid body generally explodes into dust before reaching the earth. There seems to be no direct relationship between an influx of meteorites and the annual occurrences of so-called meteor showers which radiate from a fixed point in the sky and originate from comets. Nevertheless, the nucleus of a comet may consist of a swarm of meteorites. The tiny planets called asteroids are bodies like meteorites.

Meteorites move at varying speeds, up to a calculated 44 miles per second, according to whether they arrive between midnight and noon and so hit the earth head-on with maximum velocity, or arrive between noon and midnight, when they may be barely able to catch up with the earth as it circles the sun at 18.5 miles a second. Upon striking the atmosphere they are immediately retarded, and many of them drop with no more speed than any other stone would have if it fell freely under the influence of gravity. Fragile meteorites weighing several pounds fell on thin ice near Hessle, Sweden, on New Year's Day, 1869, without breaking either themselves or the ice.

The lights and sounds that accompany a falling meteorite likewise vary from slight to violent. Among the visible effects are luminous clouds, stabbing streaks of many-colored light, and vivid sparks of flame. The sounds have been frequently described as resembling hissing, crackling, or the booming of thunder or of cannon. The fearsome spectacle of the Iowa meteor that left 460 pounds of stones near Homestead on the evening of February 12, 1875, was related by an observer in statements such as the following: "From the first the light of the meteor could hardly be tolerated by the naked eye turned full upon it . . . its light was not steady, but sparkled and quivered . . . vapor would seem to burst from the body of the meteor like puffs of steam from the funnel of a locomotive . . . after the dazzling, terrifying, and swiftly moving mass of light had extinguished itself in five sharp flashes, five quickly recurring reports were heard . . . blended with the explosions came hollow bellowings and rattling sounds, mingled with a clang and clash and roar that rolled slowly southward as if a tornado of fearful power was retreating upon the meteor's path . . . many men and animals were overcome with fear."

## METEORITES AND THE ORIGIN OF THE EARTH

These wondrous stones from the sky are the only objects that we have ever been able to see and touch and weigh and analyze that have their origin outside of our own planet. Their significance is revealed as we realize that they may be a vital clue to one of science's major mysteries—the origin of the earth. No one theory of this origin is universally accepted, but all theories give serious attention to the part that meteorites may have played.

The newest of the more complete theories, worked out mathematically by Dr. Carl F. von Weizsäcker, a German astrophysicist, proposed that meteorites represent a crystallization of the same matter that accumulated to form the earth and the other planets. The crystals are supposed to be the products of the condensation of a gaseous disk, which was derived from an earlier envelope of gas rotating around the sun.

More recently, it has been assumed that the solar system was formed by the condensation of a cold cloud of cosmic dust and gas. The parent body of meteorites has been thought by some to have been of planetary size; by others, of asteroidal size; and by others, of two successive generations, one of lunar size and one of asteroidal size.

The now-abandoned planetesimal hypothesis of Thomas C. Chamberlin and Forest R. Moulton of the University of Chicago was given its name because it described the earth as an accretion of solid particles of small size (planetesimals or miniature planets) which cooled from gases pulled away from the sun during its close encounter with a passing star.

Several curious facts have turned the attention of geologists and astronomers to meteorites in their search for a solution to this vast problem. The most obvious fact is that typical metallic meteorites, composed largely of iron and nickel, have the same density as the interior of the earth. Now, no one has ever explored the center of the earth and doubtless no one ever will, but by determining the gravitational attraction of the earth for the heavenly bodies its weight has been calculated at some 6,000,000,000,000,000,-000,000 tons. Its over-all density is known to be 5.5 and the density of the surface rocks is 2.7; hence the average density of the rest of the earth must be considerably higher and may be compared with the value of 7.7 for metallic meteorites. (The earth's density at the very center is probably very close to 16, considering the great pressures that must prevail there.)

On this basis, since the earth is believed (from the evidence given by the movement of earthquake waves) to be solid—at least down to the outside of the core—the inner core itself is likely to be a mass of nickel-iron. The studies on meteorites by Dr. Harrison Brown and Dr. Claire Patterson, carried on at the Institute for Nuclear Studies at the University of Chicago, have shown that meteorites seem to have once been under the same high pressures and temperatures that would prevail in the interior of a good-sized planet. If so, meteorites represent the remains of another planet like the earth, which must have broken up in some gigantic celestial collision or explosion.

Another interesting discovery is that measurements of radioactivity in meteorites and in terrestrial rocks show a startling correlation in their ages. Both meteorites and the oldest known rocks of the earth are over three and one-half billion years old. By measuring their speed and analyzing their chemical composition it has been established that meteorites evidently belong to the solar system, all the members of which, whatever their manner of origin, must have come into existence at about the same time.

Meteorites are rocks, whether considered as the building matter of much of the earth or merely as aggregates of minerals.

## KINDS OF METEORITES

Meteorites are broadly classed according to the relative proportions of their metallic and stony components. The metallic parts are the most typical because they differ so markedly from ordinary surface rocks.

**Iron Meteorites.** Iron meteorites or siderites (also called "irons") consist almost entirely of iron alloyed with varying percentages of nickel, although some cobalt and a little copper are always present. When sawed open, polished, and etched with dilute acids, most of these meteorites show an intricate crystalline structure, corresponding to the iron-nickel minerals called kamacite and taenite, and an intergrowth of the two known as plessite. The outside of this kind of meteorite may have almost any shape; the surfaces are more or less pitted with strange "thumb marks" and are coated with a skin of black magnetite, which oxidizes brown. Underneath is a thin layer of iron that was highly heated or even melted during the flight of the specimen through the air.

**Stony Meteorites.** At the opposite extreme are the stony meteorites or aerolites (also called "stones"), consisting of

Fig. 27—The Gladstone, New Mexico aerolite. This 110-pound stony meteorite was not identified until 14 years after it was plowed up. (*Courtesy of Harvey H. Nininger, American Meteorite Museum.*)

silicate minerals with small amounts of nickel-iron, which either spreads through the piece as a network or is scattered around in blobs or scales. The most abundant mineral in this type of meteorite is enstatite, a kind of pyroxene. Other important minerals are bronzite, hypersthene, and olivine. Also important are other pyroxenes, magnetite, chromite, and plagioclase (a group of feldspars); some glass is usually present. These meteorites are irregularly rounded and have a thin skin that is black and glassy.

Fig. 28—Slice of the Brenham pallasite, a meteorite revealing grains of olivine in a polished mesh of iron-nickel. (*Courtesy of Harvey H. Nininger, American Meteorite Museum.*)

**Stony-Iron Meteorites.** Intermediate in composition to the above types are the stony-iron meteorites or siderolites. A most interesting variety are the pallasites, named after Peter Simon Pallas, a German naturalist who made an historic voyage through Russia and Siberia in 1769. Pallasites are quickly recognized by their spongelike mesh of nickel-iron enclosing about an equal amount of large rounded crystals (called chondrules) of olivine.

**Tektites.** A very different kind of celestial visitors are the tektites. They are rounded bits of bottle-green to blackish glass which are known by several regional and local names according to the places where they are found. Moldavite from Bohemia and Moldavia is the best-known variety of tektite. Other sources are Texas, Borneo, Java, Tasmania, and the Nullarbor Plain of southern Australia, where the tektites occur throughout an area of two million square miles.

Tektites may have resulted from the impact of meteorites or the skipping action of an asteroid along the earth's surface. Because of their odd occurrence and the peculiar surface markings and rounded shapes that suggest a prolonged whirling motion, an origin outside the earth (even from the moon) has been proposed for tektites.

Besides the minerals already mentioned, a long list of others have been identified in meteorites. Most of these minerals, except probably ten, are also found in earth rocks. The ten exceptions are the following: schreibersite, a metallic white phosphide of iron and nickel; daubreelite, a metallic black chromium-iron sulfide; oldhamite, a transparent brown calcium sulfide; osbornite, a yellow titanium nitride; moissanite, a silicon carbide like carborundum; clinoenstatite, a magnesium silicate of the pyroxene group; clinohypersthene, a magnesium-iron silicate of the same group; merrillite, a phosphate belonging to the apatite group; weinbergite, a black silicate; and phosphorus, in native form. Of these, clinoenstatite, clinohypersthene, and merrillite may possibly also be of terrestrial origin; in addition, there is maskelynite, apparently a re-fused feldspar, and kosmochlor, a silicate of uncertain status.

Native gold occurs in the Wedderburn (Australia) iron meteorite and the Melrose (New Mexico) and Atlanta (Louisiana) stony meteorites. Native copper has been found in the Garnett (Kansas) and Richardton (North Dakota) stones, the Xiquipilco (Mexico) iron, and other meteorites. Minute diamonds were first observed in meteorites in 1888 in the Novo-Urei (USSR) stone and have been identified in the Canyon Diablo meteorite since 1891.

All except five of the chemical elements have been detected in meteorites, but no new one has been found besides those existing in the earth. Twenty-eight elements are abundant enough to be mentioned; fluorine and the strongly radioactive elements are remarkably scarce compared to their abundance in terrestrial rocks.

## METEORITE FALLS

Dr. Harvey H. Nininger, the noted meteorite detective, who has been directly responsible for the discovery of more meteorite falls than any other person who has ever lived, plots their paths or trajectories as they speed through the air and determines where they may have fallen. He gathers reports from eye witnesses living in scattered places and puts the separate bits of information together to build up a complete story.

An observer in a certain town may have seen the meteor traveling in an arc which he describes as best he can recall; and another person on a farm somewhere else remembers its having gone in a different direction. The various paths are then drawn on a map and the region where they approximately intersect is then searched carefully, with inquiries made at every opportunity to find someone who may know more about possible falling stones. It is customary to name meteorites after the locality where they occur, as

Johnson City, Putnam County, and Willow Creek; the name of a nearby important city is preferred.

The majority of meteorites have been found by farmers plowing their fields. Most of these specimens are naturally the metallic kinds because in weight and appearance they are conspicuously different from the rest of the stones lying on the ground. In many instances interesting and even valuable meteorites have been used for such prosaic purposes as doorstops and paperweights before their unique identity was learned. Road excavations are a likely source of meteorites, and others have been recovered from mines (as at Hayden Creek, Idaho) and wells (at Kokomo, Indiana), from the foundations of buildings (in Grand Rapids, Michigan, and Kansas City, Missouri), and even dragged up in a fish net from the bottom of Lake Okeechobee, Florida.

Of course, those meteorites that are actually seen to strike the earth have a better chance of being picked up. This was the story of the 14-pound stony meteorite that fell July 6, 1924 at Johnstown, Colorado, just behind a funeral procession. It was even more true of the stone that injured a man at Mhow, India, on February 16, 1827, and the 10-pound iron that stunned another man by the concussion at Nedagolla near Madras in the same country on January 23, 1870. The climax to date of personal injury was inflicted by the 9-pound stony meteorite that fell into a house in Sylacauga, Alabama, on November 30, 1954, striking a woman as she lay on a couch. A 2-pound stony meteorite at Kilbourne, Wisconsin, on June 16, 1911 crashed through a barn roof; a 4-pound stone at Benld, Illinois, on September 29, 1938 penetrated the roof of a garage and the top of an automobile, coming to rest in the seat cushion; a 35-pound iron at Braunau, Bohemia, punched a hole in the roof of a house on July 14, 1847, dropping into a room where three children were sleeping. A meteorite was reported to have been seen to hit and set fire to a house in Tulsa, Oklahoma, on August 11, 1945.

Nearly seven hundred other falls and groups of falls have been witnessed, to the obvious consternation of persons in the vicinity. Some of the stories related by such observers border on the grotesque. Fantastic events on the earth and strange apparitions in the sky, including men wearing crowns and royal robes, are recorded in the lore of meteorites.

Both hot and cold meteorites have been reported. Coming, as they do, from outer space, where their temperature is virtually at the freezing point, they pick up only a little warmth from the sun. Some have fallen on dry straw or grass without charring them, and others have been described as intensely cold when touched. The metallic meteorites may, however, become warm enough by friction to feel hot when handled soon after landing—an impression which would likely be exaggerated as the tale was told and retold in later years. Yet there was the Tulsa meteorite!

The simultaneous descent of several individual meteorites is referred to as a shower. To record a dozen or more specimens at a time is not uncommon. The shower of July 19, 1912 at Holbrook, Arizona, brought down an estimated 16,000 stones, and the shower—more nearly a cloudburst!—of stones at Pultusk, near Warsaw, Poland, on January 30, 1868, numbered approximately 100,000, the largest weighing 20 pounds. Reliable figures apply, of course, only to meteorites actually recovered; the larger ones may bury themselves too deeply. The original of these groups of meteorites is believed to be a single mass that broke up during its passage through the atmosphere of the earth or exploded upon impact with the ground. The jagged edges of the two splendid Chupaderos meteorites exhibited in Mexico City, for example, would fit perfectly if joined together.

**Identification of Meteorites.** How to identify meteorites after they have been found is a worthwhile question, for these rocks are useful to scientists and may even bring a respectable price to the fortunate finder. Appearance is too risky to be relied upon by the novice, though the brown (black when fresh) fusion crust, the thumb-mark pittings due to melting, and the delicate thread lines evidently due to ancient fracturing are fairly distinctive when they are present. Stony meteorites are generally characterized by a broken texture underneath their dark surface, so that they have been likened to the crust of cracked-wheat bread. Most meteorites are heavier than terrestrial rocks of similar appearance, and most are magnetic.

Stony meteorites almost invariably reveal the presence of sharp grains of metal when felt with the finger or when an edge is ground against a revolving carborundum wheel or other abrasive. The metal can be indented by pressing a needle against it, whereas most other minerals crumble to powder. Only a very few known meteorites have failed to show some metal. A chemical test for nickel is likewise recommended, inasmuch as this element is always alloyed with meteoric iron; it occurs also with most terrestrial iron (which is an uncommon mineral) but not very often in other metallic substances. The nickel test is beautiful to watch and extremely sensitive. A fragment of the specimen is detached and dissolved in nitric acid, after which ammonium hydroxide (or household ammonia) is added until a good quantity of a fluffy brown substance (iron hydroxide) appears. When this is filtered off, a few drops of an organic solution called dimethylglyoxime causes bright scarlet needles to gather, proving the presence of nickel.

Remarkable patterns of fine parallel lines called Neumann lines and intersecting bands called Widmanstätten figures are brought to light when the surfaces of two of the three main types of iron meteorites are polished and etched with dilute acid. These are due to wide plates of kamacite, narrow plates of taenite, and a filling of plessite. This structure is not known in any natural metal formed on the earth.

**Meteorite Craters.** On the level desert plain between Winslow and Flagstaff, along U.S. Highway 66 in Arizona, gapes the immense hole known as Meteor Crater. Reaching 4,250 feet from rim to rim and open to a depth of 570 feet,

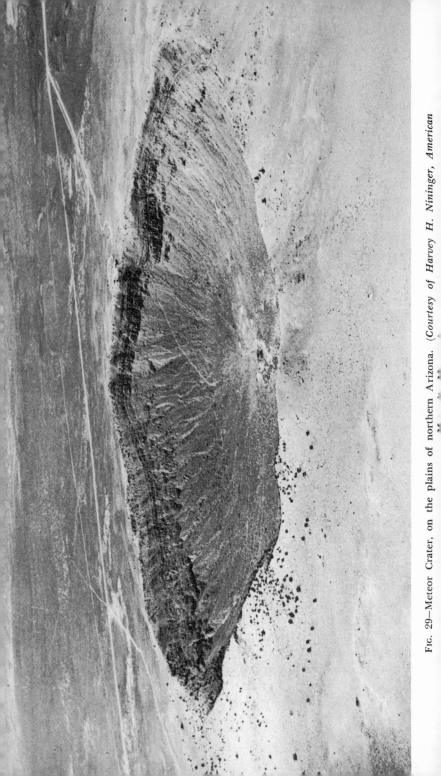

Fig. 29—Meteor Crater, on the plains of northern Arizona. (*Courtesy of Harvey H. Nininger, American*

this hole was created by the impact of a gigantic meteorite in prehistoric time, now estimated at about 22,500 years ago. Millions of tons of pulverized sandstone have more than half filled the original excavation and, together with fragments ranging up to boulders the size of a house, have been thrown as far as half a mile away, building up a rim (averaging 150 feet high) around the crater. Thousands of meteorites, the largest weighing 1,409 pounds, have been picked up within two and one-half miles of the crater, and millions of metallic or oxidized fragments still remain. A few of them are especially interesting as specimens owing to their sporadic content of tiny diamond crystals which tear apart the grinding wheel.

On the morning of February 12, 1947, for the second time in the twentieth century, an enormous meteorite plummeted to earth in the open spaces of Siberia. It produced a cluster of more than 100 craters, some being 90 feet wide and 40 feet deep, at Ussuri in the Sikhote-Alin Mountain Range, about 200 miles north of Vladivostok. The air that was compressed and heated ahead of the falling meteorite shattered the solid rock beneath it; trees were uprooted by the shock and thrown several miles. The earlier and greater cataclysm took place on June 30, 1908, between the Lena and Yenessi rivers. Only a few charred carcasses remained from a herd of 1,500 reindeer gathered near the spot where the meteorite landed. The fall left a group of broad, shallow holes which were not discovered until 20 years later, so desolate is this part of the world.

Thirty individual craters or clusters of craters with associated meteoritic material are known; they are found on every continent. Some American craters are at Haviland, Kansas; Odessa, Texas; and Kentland, Indiana. The thousands of oval depressions situated on the coastal plain of North Carolina, South Carolina, and Georgia, and known as the Carolina bays, have been assigned a meteoritic origin but this is doubtful. The great craters on the moon—50 miles or more in diameter with rims up to 4 miles high—

may be scars left by meteorites that had plunged onto its surface unhindered by any atmosphere. They may indicate what the earth looked like in past ages.

The discovery in 1960 of natural coesite, and in 1962 of stishovite (both high-pressure forms of silica) and the recognition of shattercones as of shock origin have provided a new means of identifying craters caused by meteoritic impact. They are undoubtedly much more abundant than had been suspected and have recurred throughout geologic history.

**The Largest Meteorites.** The two largest known meteorites weigh about 60 and 34 tons, respectively. The heaviest of them, named the Hoba West, a rectangular metallic mass unusually rich in nickel, lies where it was found in 1920, near Grootfontein, South-West Africa. The largest iron ever seen to fall is the Cabin Creek meteorite, with a weight of 107 pounds, which landed near a house in Arkansas on March 27, 1886. The largest stony meteorite is the Paragould, which fell in Arkansas on February 17, 1930; the main piece is in the Chicago Museum of Natural History and weighs 818 pounds. At the other extreme from these is the smallest meteorite that constitutes an entire fall; this is the Mühlau (Austria) meteorite, weighing less than a fifth of an ounce.

The second of the two largest meteorites is the giant called "The Tent" by the Eskimos around Cape York in Greenland. Fancifully christened Ahnighito after the name of Commander Robert E. Perry's daughter, it is the biggest of three metallic meteorites brought from that northern outpost in 1895 and 1897 by Perry and now kept in the American Museum of Natural History, New York. Legends of the natives had a man, his wife, their dog, and their tent dispossessed from their home in the sky and sent back to earth as useful lumps of iron. From "The Woman" were chipped pieces for fashioning into arrowheads, knives, and other sharp objects. The source of this material, said to come from an iron mountain, had been sought by every polar expedition since Captain John Ross first learned about it in 1818.

A fourth specimen was recovered not far away in 1913. The largest piece, representing the man, has never been located.

**Worship of Meteorites.** The Eskimos were not the only people to regard highly certain historic meteorites and even to worship them. The sacred "Black Stone" of Mecca is almost certainly a meteorite. The Casas Grandes meteorite in the United States National Museum in Washington is a metallic meteorite of 3,407 pounds that was found wrapped in mummy cloth in a Montezuma ruin in the state of Chihuahua, Mexico, in 1867. Modern Indians had been in the habit of taking offerings to the two large metallic meteorites (totaling 4,814 pounds) found in 1922 at Navajo, Arizona. Similar reverence was paid to the 386-pound Iron Creek metallic meteorite of Alberta, Canada, first described in 1872 as "a medicine stone of surpassing virtue among the Indians far and wide." In Europe several famous meteorites were treasured in churches and town halls as objects of veneration because they were seen descending from heaven. The earliest of all recorded meteorites that was seen to fall and is still preserved came down in a wheat field near Ensisheim, Alsace, on November 16, 1492, and is in the town hall there. Accounts of several ancient rains of stones are mentioned in the Bible.

Perhaps because of this association with religion or else with local superstition, scientists were slow to recognize the possibility of such an event as an arrival of meteorites from outer space; President Jefferson was not the only doubter. After Jerome de la Lande, an astronomer, and Father Bachelay had described the fall of meteorites, a commission was appointed to investigate the matter but still expressed disbelief. On April 26 in the year 1803, however, more than 2,000 stones peppered the earth near the village of L'Aigle, France, and settled the question with finality.

# 13

# Ores and Metals

The words ore and metal go together like chicken and egg. An ore is a rock or mineral deposit from which a metal may be extracted profitably. Thus the word ore has partly a technical meaning and partly a commercial one. When the cost of mining increases as the mine gets deeper, or some other factor changes unfavorably, a mineral deposit may cease to be classed as an ore without undergoing any actual change. On the other hand, as improved processes of mining or extraction are discovered, or as the price of a metal rises (as gold did in 1934), an idle mineral deposit may turn into a flourishing mine, and the previously worthless rock will now be profitable, becoming an ore.

## SOURCES OF ORES

An ore may, as already stated, be either a rock or a mineral. Granite with veins of native gold distributed through it is an example of an ore that is a rock, while the huge masses of hematite and native copper in the Lake Superior region are examples of ore minerals of iron and copper, respectively. We do not speak of an ore of coal or an ore of diamonds, because the products obtained are not metals. Some ore minerals yield more than one metal; galena, for instance, is the chief ore of lead, but in the Rocky Mountains it often contains valuable amounts of silver also. Stannite always contains both copper and tin. The ocean, which has yielded magnesium commercially, ranks as the greatest ore body on our planet, although it is usually not thought of in this way. A cubic mile of ordinary sea water contains more than five million tons of metallic magnesium.

**Veins.** The most typical occurrence of ores is in veins. These are so called because they appear to coil through the rock as veins do beneath the human skin. Ore in veins is the sort that the average person has in mind when he thinks of minerals on the walls of a mine. Veins occupy cracks or fissures that were already in existence before the mineral matter came in and filled them. The time difference between a vein and the enclosing rock was recognized long ago by a Saxon physician and scholar called Georg Bauer, though better known now by his Latin name Agricola. In his famous book *De Re Metallica,* published in 1556 (and translated in 1912 by Herbert Hoover and Mrs. Hoover), Agricola expressed himself impatiently: "To say that lodes (veins) are of the same age as the earth itself is the opinion of the vulgar."

Many veins branch and diverge like limbs on a tree; others are linked together like roads at a braided intersection; and still others run in pairs or sets. Some veins shrink and then bulge again from place to place; this characteristic, called pinching and swelling, makes them resemble a string of sausages. Veins range from a fraction of an inch to many miles in length. The group of veins in the tremendously rich silver deposits of the Comstock Lode in Nevada extends 4 miles; other fissure veins are still longer, and a barren quartz vein in Bavaria has been measured for 87 miles. The Champion Lode, producer of $450,000,000 in gold in the Kolar gold field of India, descends for a depth of more than 8,860 feet. The Morro Velho mine in Brazil, once the world's deepest mine, has given up $100,000,000 in gold from a single ribbon of ore over 2 miles long and extending more than 7,500 feet below the surface level. Vast treasures in precious and base metals have been won from ore veins, including those at Potosí in Bolivia and Butte in Montana, two of the richest mining areas in the world.

The waste material accompanying the useful minerals

is called gangue. Most gangue consists of nonmetallic minerals, such as quartz, calcite, and barite, but it may include some metallic minerals of little value, such as pyrite. Some kinds of gangue are used for miscellaneous purposes and so may have a certain monetary value at times, but such gangue is considered a by-product, hardly in the same class with lead or zinc or other valuable metals.

Most ore and gangue minerals have entered the veins from below, rising from unknown depths after being expelled as gases or liquids from a magma which is cooling and solidifying to become an igneous rock (see page 65). Ore deposits usually form far beneath the surface, the fluids having been exhausted of their mineral contents well before they reach the outer air; any veins that are exposed today have usually been revealed by the processes of erosion which have stripped off the overlying rocks.

As erosion continues, the veins also are destroyed and their minerals are removed. Some of the minerals are dissolved and carried away in solution, while others remain in place but weather into substances that are more stable in the new environment. Some minerals, however, possess certain desirable properties that enable them to maintain their identity in spite of weathering or erosion. These are transported downstream and eventually accumulate in a secondary mineral deposit, called a placer. In this way part of the native gold from the veins of the Mother Lode went into the placer deposits of the western slope of the Sierra Nevada in California.

**Placers.** Minerals that become concentrated in placer deposits must be heavy, mechanically durable, and chemically stable. The heavier a mineral is, the more readily it settles out of moving water. Thus, native gold and platinum, being the two heaviest of all minerals, will quickly drop to the bottom of a stream wherever the current slackens a bit as the water rounds a bend or strikes an obstruction in the channel. Quartz and the other light minerals are meanwhile swept downstream. In this way Nature produces a sorting and concentration such as man seeks to emulate when he mines, crushes, and concentrates ores. Nearly perfect examples of separation by water—this time by waves and currents—are seen in beach placers, where narrow stringers of black magnetite or chromite grains, which have been washed into position along the shore, lie in sharp contrast to the white sand surrounding them.

A placer mineral may be durable on account of its hardness, so that it resists wearing away, as do diamond and other gem stones. Or it may be tough, so that it is not easily shattered by blows, as is true of cassiterite, the chief ore of tin. Or, as any of the native metals, it may be malleable, so that it flattens instead of breaking apart. Chemical stability prevents a mineral from weathering and dissolving when exposed to the atmosphere and ground waters.

**Replacement.** Ore-bearing solutions that rise from a cooling magma not only fill open cavities in the overlying rocks, thereby producing veins as already described, but may also enter the solid rock itself and substitute for it. This important process of ore formation is called replacement. It is accomplished as the old rock slowly dissolves and the new material is added in its stead, atom for atom. We may compare replacement to removing clay bricks from a wall one at a time, each being exchanged for a metal brick, so that the pattern of the wall stays the same but the building material gradually becomes very different.

A familiar example of replacement (except that metals and ores are not involved) is petrified wood. The original woody tissue has changed to stone. In a similar fashion enormous bodies of worthless rock have been replaced by an equal volume of ore minerals. At Rio Tinto in Spain, for instance, a deposit formed by replacement contains over 500 million tons of pyrite carrying valuable amounts of gold and copper, which have been mined for 3,000 years. In other localities the solutions have spread out through the host rock, substituting new ore only in certain favorable spots, these perhaps being scattered over a huge area. The great copper mine at Chuquicamata, Chile, is reported to have some 850 million tons of such low-grade disseminated ore still available for mining. Of the various kinds of rock, limestone is especially susceptible to being replaced, inasmuch as it is readily soluble in acid solutions.

## IMPORTANT METALS AND THEIR ORES

The rest of this chapter will discuss briefly some of the most important metals and their ores, including sources and industrial uses.

**Gold.** Gold predominates over all other metals in the esteem of the human race. It has certainly been the most sought after, at least since the first recorded mining adventure by Jason and his Argonauts who sailed in the ship Argo to search for the Golden Fleece, the sheepskin in which the inhabitants of Colchis caught the gold dust too fine to be recovered otherwise.

Gold is obtained from a variety of minerals, but most of it comes as native gold. Exquisite fernlike groups of crystals, delicately coiled wires, and irregular plates of bright gold are prized in every mineral collection that is fortunate enough to contain them. When gold is washed downstream it may collect in placers as nuggets, which represent pieces originally from veins, now rounded and flattened by the moving water. The Welcome Stranger nugget—dug from the soil at Ballarat, Australia, in 1869 by a weary miner who struck it with a pick as he sat down to rest under a tree— weighed 2,280 ounces or 190 pounds. (Gold, incidentally, is calculated at 12 ounces to the pound, instead of the 16 used for most purposes; hence, the old question, "Which weighs more, a pound of gold or a pound of feathers?" is answered to the advantage of the feathers.) The largest nugget from the Yukon weighed 85 ounces. At the opposite extreme is so-called flour gold, which is so minute that in the Snake River of Idaho some of it has been estimated to require 8 million individual particles to be valued at one cent.

By far the richest gold region on earth is the fabulous Witwatersrand, centering around Johannesburg in South Africa, which has given up over 14 billion dollars worth since its discovery in 1886. Some of the mines are so deep (over 9,000 feet) that they must be air cooled. Gold from an air-conditioned mine seems indeed the epitome of luxury! The largest single gold mine in the Western Hemisphere is the Homestake Mine in the Black Hills of South Dakota.

Gold is a most independent substance. It alloys or mixes with a few other metals, especially silver, but in nature it combines chemically to any extent with only one other element, tellurium. Compounds of gold and tellurium, however, are highly significant in several widely separated regions of the world. Calaverite is a gold telluride mineral found abundantly in the Cripple Creek district of Colorado and at Kalgoorlie, Western Australia. Sylvanite is a gold-silver telluride from the same places and also from Transylvania, which is now a part of Rumania. Krennerite is another important gold telluride, hessite is a silver telluride, and petzite, like sylvanite, is a silver-gold telluride. Extraordinary specimens of hessite from the Altai Mountains in Siberia have been described as a cubic foot in size. These tellurides are usually associated with one another, and are pretty much restricted to three main regions, namely, Colorado, Western Australia, and Transylvania. Interestingly, none of these minerals is gold colored, but when heated they all give off tellurium as a dense smoke, and the gold or gold-silver alloy is "sweated out" so that it sits conspicuously on the surface of the specimen.

Another major source of gold is in a number of sulfide minerals, in which the gold is merely mixed physically with the base metals. In Arizona, for instance, considerable gold is extracted from copper ores, and in Idaho from lead ores. Pyrite (iron sulfide) also yields gold in many places.

The "fineness" or purity of natural gold is expressed in parts per thousand, like baseball "percentages." The rest of the thousand is practically all silver but may include some trifling copper or iron alloyed with the gold. Thus, 850 fine, the average quality of California vein gold, means that there are 85 parts of pure gold to 15 parts of silver. Gold containing over 20 per cent silver is known as electrum; it reveals its silver content by its paler yellow color.

The karat mark on gold jewelry is an indication of the number of parts in 24 that are pure gold, the rest being metals added to give the desired hardness or color to the manufactured article. For example, 24K is pure gold, while 12K is half gold; most American rings are 10K, 14K, or 18K, and the now-extinct gold coinage of the United States ran to 21.6K, equivalent to 900 fine in the other method of reckoning. (This kind of karat should not be confused with the word spelled carat, which is a unit of weight used for gems.)

The use of gold for coins and jewelry is too well known to need elaborate discussion. The decorative and ornamental arts employ gold leaf for plating, inlaying, and lettering. For this purpose no other metal can cover so much surface as gold, which can be beaten into translucent sheets requiring a quarter of a million to make a pile one inch thick. Dentists, glassmakers, and chemists also use gold in their occupations. In general, few substances are as useless as gold, but nothing else has tempted man to so many acts of violence, feats of daring, journeys of exploration, and efforts at community settlement. Gold, indeed, has been the forerunner of civilization in most distant lands.

**Silver.** A second precious metal, silver, parallels gold in many respects. It, too, was highly prized by ancient peoples and has been extensively used for money and adornment. The search for it was instrumental in opening up the New World, and from the mines of Latin America has come so vast a flood of silver that this metal might well be considered a native product of the Western Hemisphere, though known elsewhere long before.

The sources of silver are also much like those of gold. They include native silver, certain distinctive silver compounds, and base-metal sulfides in which silver exists as microscopic grains of metallic silver or other silver minerals. In spite of the fact that over fifty different minerals contain appreciable amounts of silver, few mines are operated solely for this metal. Mostly it is obtained as a by-product of gold, copper, lead, and zinc mining; the silver helps to make the operation more profitable.

Native silver occurs in magnificent groups of crystals resembling, except in color, those of gold and copper. Among the choicest of such crystals are the specimens from the old mines at Kongsberg, Norway, which were worked for several hundred years, furnishing the metal that made Swedish silver-craft famous. Huge chunks of native silver have been taken from the Mollie Gibson mine at Aspen, Colorado. About 1890 a nugget weighing 1,840 pounds and consisting of over 90 per cent silver was hauled to the surface by a chain, because it was too large to be placed in a mine bucket. The Cobalt district in Ontario is noted for the

Fig. 30—Native silver in heavy wires from the mines of Kongsberg, Norway, which supplied metal for the famous Swedish silver. (*Courtesy of Ward's Natural Science Establishment.*)

"silver sidewalk" of the La Rose mine, which was almost solid silver 100 feet long and 60 feet thick; a slab weighing 1,640 pounds is now on display in the Parliament Building in Toronto. Tightly matted wires of silver are a familiar feature of the ores at Aspen. Surprisingly, very little silver seems to be recovered from placers, except the silver that is alloyed with gold in nuggets.

The list of silver minerals is a long one. The highest content of silver (except, of course, native silver) occurs in argentite, which miners often call "silver glance"; this silver sulfide is sectile, meaning that it can be cut with a knife into thin shavings about as easily as a piece of lead. Argentite contributed munificently to the 400-million-dollar production at the Comstock Lode in Nevada and to the half-billion dollars worth of silver found since 1548 at Guanajuato, Mexico.

Cerargyrite, or horn silver, is likewise sectile; this silver-chloride mineral looks like horn or wax and is usually pearl gray, darkening rapidly to a violet-brown color when exposed to light, as silver salts do on photographic film. The upper veins of Cerro de Potosí, Bolivia, contained huge amounts of cerargyrite; here is a conical volcanic peak, rising to an altitude of 16,000 feet and virtually riddled with silver ores. It is famed as the richest mountain of silver on earth, having produced well over two billion ounces of the white metal since its discovery in 1544.

The "ruby silvers" are properly named. Transmitting deep-red light like a fiery garnet or ruby, their finest crystals resemble gem stones more than ore minerals. In an ordinary piece a red glow can be seen reflected from the broken gray surfaces, proving the specimen to be either pyrargyrite (so-called "dark ruby silver," containing antimony), or proustite ("light ruby silver," containing arsenic instead). Superb crystals of pyrargyrite have been found at Andreasberg in the Harz Mountains of Germany, and equally fine ones of proustite at Chañarcillo, Chile.

The majority of silver is obtained from the common ores

of other metals. The copper minerals tetrahedrite, chalcopyrite, bornite, and chalcocite, and the lead mineral galena all have silver-bearing varieties which together yield more of the precious metal than the straight silver minerals. For instance, the Anaconda Copper Company secures more silver as a by-product of its copper mining at Butte, Montana, than any silver company in the United States, and the great copper mine at Bingham Canyon, Utah, ranks second. The copper mine at Cerro de Pasco in Peru is the premier producer of silver in the entire world.

Silver has more industrial uses than gold, and modern research has shown that it can be made available for many additional purposes. The enormous photographic industry, including motion pictures, is based primarily upon the chemistry of a few silver compounds. Silver is the best conductor of electricity; bars of silver, in spite of their high cost, have been released by the United States government during wartime as a substitute for copper wire needed more urgently for ammunition. Tableware made of silver, either sterling or plated, is used in most homes. Reflecting the largest proportion of the light striking it, silver is the brightest of all metals, and it has sterilizing properties that may make it of value for water purification in swimming pools and filtering plants, as well as for silverware.

**Copper.** No metal except iron is more essential to modern life in peace and war than copper. The electrical industries demand most of it, particularly for wire, because of its excellent conductivity. Copper nails and sheets are widely used in buildings. Many metals have been added to copper to give it special properties. The earliest of these alloys was bronze, an alloy of copper, tin, and zinc, which was doubtlessly discovered by the accidental mixing and melting of several ores, and which became so important in human history that a significant period in civilization is known as the Bronze Age. A second indispensable metal is brass, an alloy of copper and zinc. More remarkable than either of these is a new copper alloy made by adding three per cent or less of beryllium; this amazingly strong metal shows no sign of fatigue even after a spring made from it has vibrated two billion times.

Northern Michigan boasts deposits of copper unique on our globe. Here native copper in colossal amounts occurs

Fig. 31—Curiously twisted plates of native copper with quartz from the Upper Peninsula of Michigan. (*Courtesy of Ward's Natural Science Establishment.*)

throughout a narrow belt 100 miles long and 4 miles wide in the Keeweenaw Peninsula on the southern shore of Lake Superior. Worked at intervals by a prehistoric race of Indians, this region has yielded the red metal in pieces ranging in size from tiny specks to a copper boulder weighing 420 tons, and of such purity that "lake copper" is a standard of quality. Curious rounded lumps of copper about the size of a man's head are called skulls. Associations of native copper and native silver are known as "halfbreeds."

Michigan now stands behind five other states which, led by Arizona, outstrip it as producers of copper. In these states and throughout the world the ore minerals are not native copper but various compounds of copper. One group of these minerals consists of sulfides, with appreciable amounts of iron, antimony, and arsenic. Although some of them are attractive enough in a modest way, most of them are rather ordinary-looking metallic minerals. Another group, in sharp contrast, includes some of the most strikingly colorful minerals ever found. These are so-called oxidized copper minerals, changed from primary minerals (such as a sulfide) by the action of percolating ground waters. They are unexcelled for beauty among the many representatives of the mineral kingdom. Unfortunately they are restricted by their nature to the upper parts of deposits and usually are soon mined out. A few members of each of these two groups of copper minerals are described below. Other sources of copper include that obtained commercially as a by-product of minerals such as the pyrite and pyrrhotite at Ducktown, Tennessee, which is the largest copper mine in the eastern part of the United States, and the pyrite at Rio Tinto, Spain.

Most delightful of the copper minerals to behold are the vivid green malachite and the intensely blue azurite—hydrous copper carbonates occurring together in hues that contrast wonderfully yet go together satisfyingly. Azurite, named because of its azure-blue color, sometimes grows in crystals which can alter slowly to malachite. Boldly banded malachite was carved into extravagantly fashioned bowls, jewel boxes, vases, and table tops in Czarist Russia, where it came from the Ural Mountains and was a favorite ornamental stone.

Richer in copper and a more important ore than either of these minerals is cuprite, a copper oxide also called "ruby copper" because of its fine red color. An exquisite variety of cuprite is found in brilliant hairlike tufts and is called chalcotrichite or "plush copper." Antlerite, a handsome

*Rocks and Minerals*

green mineral (hydrous copper sulfate), has been shown to be the chief ore mineral at Chuquicamata, Chile, the largest of all copper mines, having reserves of over 850 million tons of ore. Although it is soluble in water, antlerite is preserved at Chuquicamata because the Atacama Desert is one of the driest places on earth.

Bornite (a copper-iron sulfide) has the largest percentage of copper among the major sulfide ore minerals. It is a pretty mineral which miners call "peacock ore" and "purple copper ore" because of the variegated purple and blue tones that it assumes when it tarnishes from the bronze color seen only on freshly broken surfaces. Chalcopyrite, similar in composition to bornite, is a brassy looking mineral of great importance as an ore of copper; it is one of several minerals called "fool's gold" because it so readily deceives inexperienced prospectors. Chalcocite is a gray copper sulfide with a notable occurrence at Kennecott, Alaska, in the Copper River District, where colossal masses weighing tens of thousands of tons are found. Pieces of this mineral were eroded out of the original veins by a glacier and have been mined from surrounding walls of solid ice—a unique deposit.

Ordinarily a comparatively rare mineral, enargite, a copper-arsenic sulfide, is abundant at one significant locality, the famed Butte, Montana, district. Called the richest hill on earth, Butte, with its yield of two and three-quarter billion dollars, is surpassed as a producer of metals only by the Rand gold deposits in South Africa. Enargite is a gray or black mineral characterized by pronounced cleavage faces which give it a grooved appearance.

**Iron.** Iron and its principal alloy, steel, are the very backbone of civilization. An enumeration of their manifold uses would include an overwhelming proportion of every kind of object known to modern man. No nation has risen to a dominant position in the past two centuries without access to substantial resources of iron, in addition to coal.

Although a long list of minerals contain iron, the metal

of commerce is furnished by only a limited few of them. Unlike gold, silver, and copper, the native metal is rare, being confined largely to meteorites, some of which were beaten into implements by primitive races, as described in Chapter 12. Pyrite, one of the commonest iron minerals, is seldom used though it occurs everywhere, because the sulfur in it is undesirable in the reduction and treatment of iron. Neither is magnetite the most widely used ore, though it is the mineral with the largest amount of iron.

The industrial era in the United States began with the discovery in 1844 of the ancient hematite deposits in the northern part of Minnesota, Wisconsin, and Michigan, which have given up about two and one-half billion tons of ore. Hematite, meaning bloodlike, gets its name because, no matter what its first appearance, it becomes brownish red when crushed (or "streaked"). The American Indian and other peoples used this iron oxide as war paint and for other skin decoration.

Magnetite, also an iron oxide, is so named because it is strongly magnetic. An amazing variety, called loadstone, acts as a natural magnet, picking up bits of steel (see page 211). Both kinds of magnetite are found at Magnet Cove, Arkansas. Perhaps the largest deposit of highest-grade iron ore is the magnetite body in Swedish Lapland above the Arctic Circle.

A curious history is attached to the hydrogen iron oxide mineral known as goethite, named in honor of the great German poet-philosopher Goethe. Formerly, goethite was believed to be a rare mineral, while limonite, with a similar appearance and chemical composition but not crystalline, was regarded as one of the most widespread of all minerals, known in bogs and marshes throughout the world. When photographed with X-rays, however, practically all the so-called limonite has proved to be crystalline and hence is really goethite. Perhaps limonite is really just impure goethite or a mixture of various earthy substances and not a true mineral after all.

**Aluminum.** Although aluminum rates as the most abundant metal in the crust of the earth, it does not exist in a form permitting it to be recovered cheaply. Only one material, a rock called bauxite, serves as an ore of aluminum. Over 4,000 uses in thirty industries have been recorded for this metal. Light in weight, relatively strong, resistant to corrosion, and electrically conductive, aluminum is one of the miracle metals of the twentieth century. Once a rare curiosity, aluminum and its alloys today appear at every turn.

Previously thought to be a mineral, bauxite has been proved to be a mixture of various hydrous aluminum oxides, usually colored red by iron impurities. Typical specimens, with their rounded lumps in a claylike matrix, are among the simplest objects in the mineral kingdom to recognize. Requiring enormous amounts of electricity for its reduction, bauxite is transported from its source to the countries that possess sufficient power. Mining is carried on mainly in Arkansas, Dutch Guiana and British Guiana, and the Mediterranean region of Europe.

**Lead.** The Latin word for lead is *plumbum,* and so a plumber was one who laid water pipes, which, in Roman times were, as now, made of lead. Some ancient uses for this soft, heavy metal, such as coinage, have died out, while others, such as solder, have persisted to the present day. Paint manufacture employs large though decreasing amounts of lead, and the metal itself is used to make bullets and storage batteries.

Of the three minerals that are commercial sources of lead, galena is by far the most outstanding. Crystals of this lead sulfide are bright gray cubes, showing clearly the steplike cleavage along which they invariably break. Almost half of the lead production of the United States comes from southeastern Missouri, where the "lead belt" around Flat River has the greatest concentration of galena in the world. Traces of silver are almost always present in galena; where the content increases, as in Idaho, Colorado, Utah, and other western states, galena becomes one of the chief ores of silver.

The oxidation of galena changes it into two other minerals which are likewise mined as ores of lead. Anglesite is lead sulfate, and is usually found as gray masses surrounding a core of galena still preserved intact. The action of carbonated water on galena produces cerussite, which is lead carbonate. In 1876 it was discovered that heavy sand, which for years had bothered the gold placer miners in California Gulch, in central Colorado, was actually cerussite; the ensuing renewal of activity caused the establishment there of the city of Leadville. Fascinating-sounding places such as Tsumeb in South-West Africa, Broken Hill in New South Wales, and Sidi-Amor-ben-Salem in Tunisia are areas yielding superior specimens of these three lead minerals.

**Zinc.** Of the major metals, perhaps the least familiar to most persons is zinc, so generally associated with lead that the two are spoken of together. In order to make brass, the Greeks and Romans added to copper a zinc mineral without realizing the nature of the latter. Nowadays zinc is also used extensively in plating steel to prevent rust—this is called galvanizing—and in die castings and paint.

The chief ore of zinc is sphalerite, a zinc-sulfide mineral also known to miners as "zinc blende" or "black jack." Its color usually ranges from yellow to brown to black, according to the percentage of iron present. Regardless of color, the resinous luster on most specimens can be recognized at a quick glance. Sphalerite alters to smithsonite, a zinc carbonate; several peculiar varieties are appropriately named "turkey-fat ore" and "dry bone ore" because of their odd appearance. Hemimorphite, formerly called calamine, is another secondary zinc mineral, a hydrous silicate; its crystals grow in clusters and are differently shaped at opposite ends.

The dominant zinc area of the world is the Tri-State district situated where the three states of Missouri, Kansas, and Oklahoma come together. The tall white dumps of waste rock that line the countryside "like sand dunes on a desert" stand as silent witnesses to the enormous amount of material removed from beneath the soil. The largest single lead-zinc mine anywhere on earth, however, is the Sullivan mine at Kimberley, British Columbia.

At Franklin and Sterling Hill, New Jersey, an extraordinary combination of geologic events resulted in distinctive bodies of zinc ore enclosed in marble. This is a happy hunting ground for specimen collectors, yielding over 150 kinds of minerals, many of which have never been seen elsewhere. The ore minerals, common here but scarce everywhere else, are zincite (an oxide of zinc), willemite (a fluorescent green silicate of zinc), and franklinite (an oxide of zinc, manganese, and iron). These are further described in Chapter 11 on luminescent minerals. The mines are now dormant.

**Tin.** As a constituent of bronze, tin was one of the first metals used by man. During the Middle Ages it became the chief component of pewter. Otherwise, however, tin received little attention until the expansion of industry in modern times, when it became one of the major metals. Although we speak slightingly of the lowly tin can, and all of us except the younger generation remember the unglamorous "tin lizzie," tin is by no means a cheap metal. So valuable did it become during the Second World War that strenuous efforts were made to recover the bare one per cent of tin that lines the inside of the steel containers known as tin cans, and even to substitute precious silver in its place. Tin in large amounts also enters into the making of solder, terne plate, babbitt metal, type metal, and other alloys.

Tin comes predominantly from cassiterite, an interesting tin oxide mineral often called tinstone. When found as pebbles in placer gravels it is known as stream tin. Other curious forms are appropriately named wood-tin and toad's-eye tin. Superior brown or black crystals of this heavy mineral are found in England, France, New South Wales, and Bolivia. The tin veins on the Scilly Islands off the coast of Cornwall, England, were visited by the Phoenicians, who ventured there on commercial voyages and made Britain and the surrounding islands known to the ancient world as the Cassiterides or Tin Islands. The main occurrences of cassiterite and hence of tin are in the belt of placer deposits that stretches for 1,000 miles from Burma through the length of the Malay Peninsula to the islands of Indonesia.

**Ferro-alloy Metals.** Toward the end of the nineteenth century it was discovered that the addition of small quantities of certain uncommon chemical elements endow steel with remarkable new qualities. They provide it with increased hardness, tensile strength, lightness, and resistance to corrosion. Previously of little value, these substances, called ferro-alloy metals, have consequently become as essential to the steel industry as yeast is in baking bread. Alloy steels have been largely responsible for the progress of engineering and technology in the first half of the twentieth century. These ferro-alloys also have a multitude of other uses apart from their primary one—thus, manganese for glass and dry batteries, nickel for coinage and Monel metal, chromium for tanning and plating, molybdenum for dyes and ink, tungsten for filaments in electric light bulbs, vanadium for ceramic glazes, cobalt for enamel, titanium for paint.

MANGANESE. Manganese was the first ferro-alloy metal used and it is still the most important, because it is required for its cleansing or deoxidizing effect, even in the making of ordinary steel. Manganese minerals have a pronounced tendency to occur in mixtures of various black oxides, including manganite, pyrolusite, and psilomelane. Rhodocrosite is a pink manganese carbonate, and rhodonite is a pink manganese silicate. The largest manganese mine in the world is the Nsuta mine in Ghana, Africa, though the Soviet Union is probably the principal producer.

NICKEL. Nickel is obtained mainly from the mineral pentlandite, a bronze-colored sulfide of iron and nickel. The deposits at Sudbury, Ontario, yield not only about 130,000 tons of nickel annually, but also the astounding total of 130,000 tons of copper, 200,000 ounces of the platinum metals, 50,000 ounces of gold, 1,500,000 ounces of silver,

150,000 pounds of selenium, and 10,000 pounds of tellurium. In New Caledonia, the next largest producing area, the ore mineral is garnierite, a green nickel silicate.

CHROMIUM. Chromium comes from the oxide mineral called chromite, which also contains iron and can be added directly to the furnace. Originally, stainless steel used chromium alone, but now it is made with both chromium and nickel. Whereas the United States was formerly the leading producer of chromium ore, its output has declined almost to extinction, while Turkey, the Soviet Union, the **Republic of South Africa, the Philippines, and Southern Rhodesia have gained control of the market.**

MOLYBDENUM. Not easy to say or to spell, molybdenum is familiarly called "Molly" by those who mine it and work with it. Bartlett Mountain at Climax—rising to an altitude of 13,500 feet in the Colorado Rockies—is a huge body of granite riddled with small veins of a soft black sulfide mineral, molybdenite, which closely resembles graphite. This mine long monopolized the world's supply of "Molly" but it has recently been pressured to maintain its position, owing to competition from the by-product molybdenum of the vast copper pit at Bingham Canyon, Utah.

WOLFRAM. Wolfram will probably always be known in the United States as tungsten, even though chemists have internationally agreed to adopt the earlier German name. High-speed tool steels are based on the use of this metal. Four minerals furnish the wolfram of commerce, and each comes from different places. Scheelite, a white calcium tungstate, is especially interesting because of its bright fluorescence, as described in Chapter 11. Ferberite, wolframite, and huebnerite constitute a series of black or brown iron-manganese minerals of wolfram.

VANADIUM. Patronite, perhaps a black sulfide of vanadium, is produced in enormous amounts in Minasragra, Peru. A micaceous mineral referred to as roscoelite yields vanadium in the Colorado Plateaus of Utah and Colorado, where also occurs the radioactive mineral carnotite (described on page 150), which has been mined occasionally for vanadium. Vanadinite and descloizite, two other important ore minerals of vanadium, are found in attractive crystallized specimens. Another interesting source of vanadium is provided by the treatment of soot collected on ocean freighters that burn petroleum from wells in Mexico and Venezuela.

COBALT. Steel for magnets and jet airplane engines utilizes cobalt. Although several sulfide and oxide minerals can themselves provide a good deal of cobalt, more than half of the metal that is used is recovered as a by-product of copper and silver mining. The Republic of the Congo is the world's leading source of cobalt, with Northern Rhodesia in second place.

TITANIUM. An unprecedented amount of effort and money are being expended by government and industry in experimental work with titanium, resulting in the prediction that this interesting metal will come into large-scale use more quickly than did any of the other ferro-alloys. The chief minerals are ilmenite, an oxide of iron and titanium, and rutile, a titanium oxide. The recent discovery of ilmenite ore in the wilderness of Quebec has already proved this to be the largest known deposit in existence.

# 14

# Rocks and Minerals for Industry

As the list of "commercially useless" rocks and minerals steadily decreases year by year, we are fairly certain that not too many decades are apt to pass before an industrial application will be known for virtually every earth material. Some of the recent discoveries of uses for rocks and minerals that were previously regarded as probably useless resemble the Cinderella story.

**Mineral Wool.** A most interesting example is found in the prosaic field of building insulation, where protection against heat and sound is desired. Except still air, mineral wool has the lowest heat conductivity of any material, even less than cork. It is also light in weight, owing to the presence of an enormous number of tiny pockets of air trapped between thin silicate fibers, which cause it to resemble wool in appearance and make it an ideal insulator. One after another of various minerals and rocks have been used to make mineral wool by melting them in furnaces at fairly low temperatures, producing a stream of molten silicate glass, which is then sheared while cooling rapidly to prevent crystallization. This is accomplished in a number of ways according to the substances used—for example, by adding fluorspar to produce finer fibers.

Among the raw materials customarily employed for mineral wool is wollastonite, a calcium silicate mineral abundant in California. Another is glass wool made from common soda-lime glass, which gives a strong, flexible fiber that can be woven into glass fabrics. More recently research has

found that slag from iron blast furnaces is eminently suitable for making a kind of mineral wool generally known
as rock wool, thereby providing an extensive use for what
had always been regarded as just about the most utterly
worthless material imaginable.

**Magnesite.** Another interesting building material is magnesite, a mineral composed of magnesium carbonate. Heated
to caustic magnesite it is used as a stucco and for wallboard
and flooring. As a flooring material it is inexpensive, durable yet flexible, fireproof, nonshrinking, and dustless, and
it takes wax or polish. Near Chewelah, Washington, and
in the Coast Ranges and Kern County in California, magnesite exists in huge reserves, though smaller than in some
foreign countries, especially Manchuria. Now that metallic
magnesium can be extracted from sea water, the building
industry shares with the metallurgical industry the chief
remaining uses of such large deposits of this mineral.

**Clay Minerals.** With the advancement of agriculture to
the status of an applied science, the minerals that, together
with decayed foreign matter, constitute the soil are taking
on new significance. The clay minerals form the natural
laboratory in which the vital soil-forming processes take
place. These minerals comprise a group of hydrous aluminum silicates mixed with certain impurities. Kaolin, named
from a hill in China, is the most familiar of the clay minerals, which can be distinguished from one another only
by X-rays, thermal analysis, and the electron microscope.
Their common characteristic is their ability to become plastic when wet, so that they can be molded, after which they
harden permanently upon being fired. These properties
have determined the widespread use of clay since the earliest
civilizations, and are the basis of the substantial wealth-
creating ceramic industries. In the earth, however, the real
importance of the chemical decomposition of aluminous
rocks, which gives rise to the clay minerals, lies in the ways
in which the various kinds of soil originate. This study
promises rich rewards for future generations.

**Fertilizers.** The fertilizer minerals are another aspect of the farm use of earth materials. The weathering processes that change solid rock into loose soil also cause the loss of elements which are leached out by the slow percolation of water through the ground. Soils derived from certain rocks may never have had some of the elements needed for plant growth. Fertilizers can remedy both deficiencies, supplying the necessary plant nutriments. They also transform insoluble substances into a more soluble form so that they can be profitably utilized. Excessively acid or alkaline soils can be neutralized or modified as desired. Some fertilizers destroy objectionable parasites.

Many rocks and minerals function as fertilizers. Potash, formerly obtained by evaporating the leachings of wood ashes used for soapmaking, is now secured in the United States mostly from underground minerals near Carlsbad, New Mexico, and from brines at Searles Lake, California. Large beds of potash minerals occur in Germany, where Stassfurt is the best-known district.

Nitrogen compounds are also important fertilizers, but these are derived mainly from the atmosphere by synthetic processes. Mineral nitrates from Chile, however, are still used abroad to a small extent. These minerals occur as so-called caliche in the narrow desert areas of northern Chile, where rain and trees are equally rare.

The third of the three major fertilizers is phosphate. This is doubtless the most interesting because it follows a well-organized cycle. Originating in igneous rocks as the mineral apatite, it changes to soil, from which it is absorbed by plants, eaten by animals, and returned again to the soil; eventually it is dissolved by subsurface water and transported to the sea, where it is either taken up by marine life or deposited in sedimentary beds, and the cycle begins anew. When the natural phosphate rock is treated with sulfuric acid it becomes superphosphate or some other "acid phosphate," readily available for plant food. The United States and North Africa satisfy most of the world's demand for phosphate. The gravels of Florida, in which are found fossil teeth and bones of land and sea animals, yield nearly half of the total production.

**Building Stones.** Travelers stand in awe before the mighty pyramids of Egypt and Mexico, the symmetrically fashioned buildings of ancient Greece, and the splendid cathedrals of Europe. In our present century the building-stone industry seems at times to be fighting a losing battle with the purveyors of artificial products, which have less of the beauty and little of the romance of the natural building stones employed so successfully by our ancestors.

To be sure, these substitutes are all made from natural earth materials and so the total production of rocks and minerals has increased vastly over the years. Except for a small amount of wood, the modern home, office building, church, school, and factory, the highway and bridge, are all constructed of stone, clay, sand, and other common substances which occur in large bulk, together with lesser quantities of the more expensive substances covering a wide range from mica to mineral pigments.

Nevertheless, the use of what is termed in the trade "dimension stone" fluctuates considerably and has lost ground to the users of prepared products. Seldom today are buildings constructed of solid masonry; instead, thin slabs are used to encase the frameworks already erected of steel and to decorate those of concrete. At intervals a strikingly effective installation puts to shame the most skillfully devised man-made substitute and draws renewed attention of architects and contractors to the possibilities inherent in native stone. The variations in color and patterns are almost endless. Strength is increased, though cost is also, and fire hazards are reduced. Even yet the availability of natural stone is utilized for numerous interior and exterior purposes, though the amount is only a fraction of the total volume of a given structure. Steps, fireplaces, sills, baseboards, wainscoting, facings, and trim are the likeliest places to find stone even in a building that has none elsewhere.

In the classic eras of Greece and Rome the Pentelic and Parian marbles from Greece and Carrara marble from Italy reached their heights of monumental and decorative use in the glorious edifices of those Mediterranean lands. In twentieth-century United States the Barre granite from Vermont, the Indiana limestone from Bedford, Indiana, and the marble from Georgia and Vermont are among the more familiar building stones in the nation, though there are many other varieties that are specified daily by designers and builders. Larvikite, for instance, is a rich blue syenite imported for ornamental purposes at a premium price from near Laurvik, Norway; a notable example of its use in exterior decoration is the front of the Chrysler Building in New York. When the rosy travertine from Canon City, Colorado, was installed on the outside of the *Denver Post* building, a whole new market was opened up for this novel and highly attractive stone.

**Abrasives.** Entirely unrelated except in their use, a group of rocks and minerals of dissimilar composition share in common the ability to cut and polish metal, stone, plastic, and wood. They are known as natural abrasives. Like building stones they suffer from growing competition from artificial products, but these in turn are made from naturally occurring minerals.

Diamond is the pre-eminent abrasive, but several other minerals of more than average hardness are also used. Corundum, emery, and garnet rank above quartz in the scale of hardness and consequently offer advantages on that account. Besides, each of them possesses certain subtle physical characteristics that enable it to do a special job better than any other abrasive. Garnet, for example, has an exceptional capacity for finishing hard rubber and hard woods.

Named after its discovery at Cape Emeri, Greece, emery is an abrasive of particular toughness and heat resistance. It is an intimate mixture of corundum and magnetite, or corundum, hematite, and spinel, the proportions varying according to the locality. Emery from the island of Naxos,

Greece, is the hardest commercial grade; that from Aidin, Turkey, comes next; and the United States, the third-ranking producer, furnishes softer material used mostly in pastes.

A somewhat extended list of abrasives belong to the siliceous group, consisting of silica in one form or another. Sandstone, composed of grains of quartz, is the principal member of this group, and it appears in the market as pulpstones and other grindstones, millstones, and sharpening stones. Diatomaceous earth, tripoli, and pumice are among the other siliceous abrasives of natural origin and wide industrial application.

It is curious to note that numerous soft minerals are eminently suitable for abrasive purposes because they have a high melting point and can be used for polishing gem stones and buffing metals, as well as for general scouring and cleaning. Feldspar is the chief constituent of one leading nationally advertised household powder. Even talc, the softest of all minerals, is used to polish rich grains, leather, and soft metals, and through its exceedingly high fusing temperature it has proved able to abrade diamond, the hardest of all known substances.

**Asphalt.** Neither a true mineral nor rock, asphalt nevertheless occurs as a bonding agent in sandstone, shale, and marl, and as a filling in the openings of limestone. In the famous 114-acre Pitch Lake at Brighton in Trinidad and Guanoco Lake in Venezuela, this interesting hydrocarbon forms unique pools, and in these places asphalt might properly be regarded as a rock substance, since it constitutes a substantial aspect of the structure of the earth (see page 3). In the days of the Spanish conquistadors asphalt was widely used for calking ships, and many sixteenth-century English and French pirates forced entry into Lake Maracaibo, Venezuela, to get pitch.

Asphalt is the plastic material left behind when the more volatile fractions of petroleum seepages evaporate into the air. A little heat is sufficient to melt even the hardest specimens of this natural bitumen. The chief use of asphalt is for paving; it is also employed in roofing, which is usually coated with granules of rock. Sandstone and other rocks highly cemented with asphalt are used directly for road-making after simply being crushed. Aside from the material in the remarkable asphalt lakes, certainly the most intriguing asphaltic substance is gilsonite, found in veins in northeastern Utah and northwestern Colorado. The few tentative uses for gilsonite of not long ago have increased to dozens of valuable ones, and new uses are being devised with frequency. It is now a source of petroleum.

**Borates.** The twenty-mule teams that brought borax from sparkling white surface crusts in Death Valley have vanished. The deposits, too, are no longer in use, having given way to more workable borate minerals and more profitable deposits. Kernite, discovered in high-grade form in 1925, is now the principal source of refined borax, which is obtained merely by dissolving kernite in water and evaporating the solution. Both kernite and natural borax occur in beds near Kramer, California, and borax is pumped from brines at Searles Lake, also in the Mojave Desert. The primary source of borate minerals seems to be the boric acid brought to the surface through gas vents and hot springs associated with volcanoes. Present-day steam vents in Italy can be observed to produce borax in this way; the condensation of superheated steam yields a solution of boric acid which evaporates to give borax.

The compounds made from borax enter into a hundred industries from food to jewelry, from medicine to carpets, from paper to tools. The antiseptic and cleansing properties of borax make it useful at home. Jet fuel uses it also.

**Fillers.** Powdered minerals that are added to manufactured products to give them, at low cost, various desired characteristics otherwise lacking are called mineral fillers. They furnish bulk, weight, opacity, and other properties to improve the appearance or durability of the product. Next to their being chemically inert, the degree of fineness and an appropriate color are probably the most essential features of the majority of fillers. Why a bargain-price shirt or sheet seems to lose so much weight after its first laundering can be explained by the presence of a filler that washes out. Books that would seem too thin for their price are printed on bulking paper. We all eat quantities of harmless but scarcely nourishing clay with our candy. As adulterants some fillers are under suspicion and others have been banned from commerce by law. Rubber, paper, and paint are among the major industries using mineral fillers.

# 15

# Oddities of the Mineral Kingdom

Some rocks and minerals exhibit odd characteristics or have extraordinary uses. This chapter will discuss briefly fifteen of these unusual substances from the earth.

**Asbestos—Mineral Silk.** Asbestos might seem to belong to the vegetable instead of the mineral kingdom, for its soft, silky fibers are so flexible that they can be spun into threads and woven into fabric. Unlike plant fibers, however, the delicate threads of asbestos are fireproof, acidproof, verminproof, and resistant to electricity and heat. Such a combination of virtues makes asbestos extremely valuable for many industrial needs. The Romans learned that it would make an everlasting lampwick and could be woven into cremation cloth which became purified in the fire.

Since ancient times literally hundreds of uses have been developed for this remarkable substance. In 1725 Benjamin Franklin owned a curious purse "made of the stone asbestos." Credit for making the first asbestos suit for firemen (in 1806) is given to an Italian noblewoman. The old-time theater curtain with the reassuring word ASBESTOS written across it in large letters represents to most persons who can remember it the most familiar use for this mineral. The long fibers are chiefly spun and woven into textiles, whereas the short ones are generally matted together and manufactured into shingles and boards for various insulating purposes. For brake linings, as an example, no substitute has yet been devised.

The term asbestos is applied to a small number of different minerals having a fibrous nature. Some are better than others or less likely to fuse when exposed to a high temperature. The choicest kind is chrysotile, a variety of the mineral serpentine; it can be heated to 5,000 degrees Fahrenheit, and a single pound of it can be spun into 32,000 feet of thread. The mines in Quebec yield over half of the world's

FIG. 32—Asbestos, the silky mineral fiber. This is the chrysotile variety of serpentine from Thetford, Quebec. (*Courtesy of Johns-Manville Sales Corp.*)

supply of chrysotile, which occurs as veins in massive serpentine. The green rock is crushed and screened; air suction pulls off the asbestos fibers in what constitutes a unique method of separating desired minerals from waste rock.

Amphibole comprises a group of minerals that have at times the characteristics typical of asbestos. Crocidolite, for example, is known as blue asbestos and is found mainly in South Africa; when oxidized to a brown color and replaced by silica it becomes the gem stone called tiger's-eye. Anthophyllite, a short and brittle kind of amphibole, is being used in a newly developed plastic insulating material. Amosite is a name coined from the initials of Asbestos Mines of South Africa, the company on whose property it was first found; although the fibers found in the Transvaal, South Africa, are splintery, some of them attain a length of 11 inches. Other asbestos amphiboles, such as tremolite and actinolite, have only minor commercial value.

**"Animal" and "Vegetable" Minerals.** Membership in the mineral kingdom ought to be even more difficult to obtain for these minerals than for asbestos. So unlike minerals do they appear that names suggesting animal and vegetable products have been given to them. (The first three referred to below belong to the amphibole group of minerals already discussed under asbestos.) Instead of silky fibers resembling flax, they are built of coarse fibers that look like leather, cork, and wood.

Mountain leather has its tough fibers interlaced to make thin flexible sheets. It is light enough to float on water and is white, gray, or yellowish in color. An especially thin variety is known as mountain paper. Leadhills, Scotland, is a source of mountain leather.

Mountain cork is similar but occurs in thicker pieces, and it, too, floats. Buckingham, Quebec, is one of the chief localities for this strange material.

Mountain wood is more compact, though also fibrous, and it looks rather like dry wood, being brown or gray.

A soft, spongy variety of calcite sometimes goes under the name of mountain milk or of rock milk. An unctuous variety of halloysite, a claylike mineral, is called mountain soap, while mountain tallow is a yellowish, waxy hydrocarbon properly called hatchettite. Mountain butter is alunogen, and mountain meal is diatomaceous earth.

In addition to these "mountain minerals" there are very many minerals having varieties with interesting, peculiar names applied to them by imaginative persons, who saw resemblances to vegetable or animal substances. Thus we have asparagus-stone, which is green apatite (surely an appropriate combination of words!); cinnamon-stone, which is grossularite garnet; dry bone ore and turkey-fat ore, which are kinds of smithsonite; feather ore, usually meant for jamesonite, though it has also been applied to stibnite, zinkenite, boulangerite, and meneghinite; feather-alum, which is halotrichite; hair salt, a silky fibrous epsomite; horseflesh ore, a good name to describe bornite; kidney ore, which is rounded hematite; and many other strange names, such as toad's-eye tin, dogtooth spar, cockscomb pyrite, bone turquoise, wood tin, rock meal, and several kinds of mineral roses.

**Loadstone—a Natural Magnet.** The earth is a huge magnet, attracting magnetized objects toward its north and south poles. When this magnetism is induced in another substance, it, too, becomes a magnet. Occasional specimens of magnetite, an iron oxide mineral, which act in this way are called loadstone. Some loadstones of exceptional power will support a large proportion of their own weight in steel objects. It is fascinating to watch this seemingly ordinary black mineral hold a string of nails, thumbtacks, paper clips, and other metal products.

When freely suspended by a string, loadstone exerts its polarity, twisting around until its south pole points to the north pole of the earth—hence the significance of its name. This property was put to good use in making the first mariner's compass, which probably consisted of a sliver of loadstone floating in a cup of water. When a compass is brought near a hanging loadstone its needle will swing toward the opposite pole, and when a piece of iron is touched to a loadstone it becomes a magnet itself.

Magnet Cove, near Hot Springs, Arkansas, furnishes loadstone of remarkable strength. Many superstitious people still carry a small piece as a supposed cure for rheumatism.

Some iron-bearing varieties of native platinum have a strong magnetic attraction for steel objects; these might well be referred to as precious loadstone.

**Calcite—Seeing Double.** Pure and transparent calcite is called Iceland spar because of its original occurrence in Iceland. This material is clear enough to read print through. The letters, however, appear doubled when the specimen is held in certain directions. As the mineral is slowly rotated, the print merges into a single row of letters and then gradually doubles again. The same is true of a dot or ruled line, which alternates between double and single status. Called double refraction, this wonderful property has been utilized for important optical purposes, although at one time it was only a source of curiosity to the ladies of the French court, who amused themselves performing simple experiments with bits of the spar.

Double refraction means the breaking up of a ray of light into two new rays. Each ray then has its own path and its own speed, sometimes its own color also. This makes possible one of the means of identifying gems, whereby the individual color of each ray is observed through a pocket-sized instrument called a dichroscope, which is primarily a holder for a piece of Iceland spar. Petrographic microscopes, the kind used by professional mineralogists, are equipped with segments of Iceland spar called nicol prisms, carefully fashioned to pass either ray of light in the desired direction.

Calcite of the usual kind, not suitable for these uses, is an extremely common mineral, widely distributed throughout sedimentary rocks and metamorphic rocks derived from them. The urgent search for clear calcite in the early months of the Second World War, for use in target sights, uncovered previously unsuspected deposits in a number of places. The largest supply of high-grade optical calcite came from northern Mexico and substantial amounts were imported from Africa. Calcite occurs in a greater variety of forms than any other mineral. No matter what its outer appearance, every crystal of Iceland spar cleaves readily into perfect rhombs, and always at the same angles.

**Star Stones.** Some minerals have the extraordinary ability of causing light to appear as starlike rays. The directions of these rays depend upon the crystal structure of the mineral, and so they are always symmetrical and oftentimes exceedingly beautiful. This effect is called asterism.

Star ruby and star sapphire are the best-liked examples of asteriated or star stones. Because these gems crystallize in an internal hexagonal pattern, the resulting rays are arranged in a sixfold manner, radiating outward from the top center of the stone. To show the brightest and sharpest stars such gems should be cut with a fairly steep rounded top, the bottom being perpendicular to the long dimension of the original crystal. Owing its existence to the deflection of light from extremely tiny needlelike inclusions of another mineral or to hollow tubes, the star is an inherent part of the stone. Consequently a single gem may be cut into any number of smaller ones, yet if properly oriented each will contain a whole star. Star sapphires are much more abundant and hence less costly than star rubies. Many of the less expensive colors, such as gray and light blue, show the clearest stars. The presence of the inclusions that cause the asterism makes complete transparency impossible, but maximum clarity is desired. Synthetic star rubies and star sapphires, closely resembling the natural ones, are a recent triumph of chemistry.

Rose quartz is another gem occasionally seen with a star of six or even twelve rays. Asterism at times appears in garnet, but as this mineral belongs to the isometric crystal system (see page 110), the star may have a fourfold pattern with 4, 8, or 12 rays, in addition to the six-sided arrangement. Fascinating spheres of garnet, which bring forward an endless succession of both kinds of stars as they are slowly rolled in one's hand, have been cut by amateur lapidaries.

Apart from the gems, there are a few other minerals that also show asterism. Among them are several members of the mica group. Whereas the stars just described are observed in reflected light, the mica stars are seen best in transmitted light, that is, when viewed through the specimen. A thin sheet of phlogopite, the magnesium mica, when held in front of a candle flame usually reveals a six-rayed star, with the rays of a less prominent star midway between the others. Phlogopite from northern New York and South Burgess, Ontario, is noted for this property, which is due to inclusions of tiny needlelike crystals of rutile or tourmaline.

Fig. 33—Phlogopite mica from Bedford, Ontario, showing asterism when held in front of a light bulb. (*Courtesy of Ward's Natural Science Establishment.*)

**Cryolite—Disappearing Stone.** The Viking explorers of
western Greenland remarked with amazement about the
mysterious heavy white stone used by the Eskimos to anchor
their kayaks. Dropped into the water it immediately became
invisible. Today we know this mineral as cryolite, a name
which means "froststone," an allusion to the appearance of
the white masses. Cryolite is a fluoride of sodium and alumi-

num. Besides being heavy it is soft; it cleaves into cubic blocks; and even a candle will fuse it. The near-disappearance of the material is due to the fact that light travels through it at about the same speed as through water and so is not bent when passing from one to the other. Consequently, cryolite is scarcely visible when immersed.

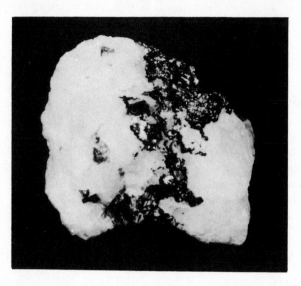

Fig. 34—White cryolite from Ivigtut, Greenland, surrounding pyrite, galena, siderite, and other associated minerals. (*Courtesy of Pennsylvania Salt Mfg. Co.*)

Cryolite really came into its own in 1886 when Charles Hall in the United States and Paul Héroult in France, each working independently, discovered that metallic aluminum could be extracted commercially by passing electricity through a bath of molten cryolite. About the beginning of the twentieth century, bauxite (see page 194) became practically the sole ore of aluminum, though cryolite continued to be used to melt the aluminum oxide obtained from bauxite. Artificial cryolite has largely replaced the natural mineral for this purpose, but additional uses for

Greenland cryolite have been developed, such as for enamel, insecticides, and opalescent glass.

Although cryolite is considered a rare mineral because it is found in only four places in the world, one of these localities contains an enormous amount. The seemingly inexhaustible quarry at Ivigtut, at the head of the narrow Arsuk Fiord in Greenland, is one of the largest deposits known of a single mineral. Other minerals are present, of course, but only a small amount of galena has been recovered for its lead and silver content. Sorting, crushing, and treatment of the cryolite take place in Copenhagen, Denmark. Some cryolite has been mined at Miask in the Ilmen Mountains of the Soviet Union, and a little is found near Sallent in the Spanish Pyrenees and on the sides of St. Peters Dome near Pikes Peak, Colorado.

**Vermiculite.** When it is heated, vermiculite, a mineral resembling mica, slowly swells like an accordian being opened or a worm crawling. This peculiar lifelike appearance has given the substance its name, which means "little worm." The process of expansion is known as exfoliation, as though scales or leaves were falling away from the main piece. They are in reality being pushed away by the expanding air and moisture trapped in the countless cells between the micaceous flakes. After being heated, therefore, vermiculite makes a highly effective insulating material to fill open spaces between the walls of buildings. Mixed with cement it serves as a lightweight aggregate, reducing the cost of construction. It is also used to pack glass for shipping and to convey fertilizer to the soil.

Biotite and perhaps other mica minerals alter to vermiculite. The most important production comes from Libby, Montana, where a large rounded hill consists almost entirely of vermiculite. Another large mine is operated in the Transvaal, Republic of South Africa, and extensive deposits are known in Brazil.

**Native Mercury.** This unique substance aptly deserves both of its common names: mercury, on account of its capri-

cious habits—for it scarcely stands still unless closely confined—and quicksilver, or living silver, for its mysterious
fleeting nature and its bright silver color. It is heavier than
lead and more than 13 times as heavy as water. It is a true
metal, the only common one that is liquid at ordinary temperatures.

Most of the mercury extensively used for medical, chemical, scientific, and industrial purposes is obtained from
cinnabar, a red mercury sulfide in which the metal is chemically combined with sulfur. Nevertheless, some native mercury occurs by itself as a mineral, either in single drops or
in small pools occupying cavities in the rock. In this way
it is found in the mercury districts of Italy, Spain, Yugo-
slavia, Bavaria, California, and Texas. These are all regions
of hot springs and recent volcanic activity.

Whereas water vaporizes to steam at 100 degrees Centigrade at sea level, mercury becomes a gas at about 350 degrees. When cooled to 39 degrees below the freezing point
of water, mercury solidifies in brilliant tin-white crystals.
This ability of mercury to stay liquid over a wide range of
temperatures has led to its best-known use, in thermometers.
The bulb and slender tube are generally referred to as the
mercury column, even though inexpensive household thermometers use a cheap substitute instead, and very costly
thermometers for scientific research may use gallium, a rare
metal that stays liquid as high as 2,000 degrees Centigrade.
The medieval alchemists were completely fascinated by
mercury, and it entered into many of their devious experiments to transmute base metals into gold. Its affinity for
gold and silver has made it valuable as a means of recovering them by amalgamation, described on page 23. During
the early years of the California gold rush the discoveries
of mercury in that state were a vital factor, often overlooked
by historians, in maintaining production by making the
gold quickly available.

Mercury is sold in steel flasks holding 76 pounds. A "Believe it or Not" cartoon by Ripley showed how a strong man

can throw a full flask of mercury across his shoulder, but not one that is only half full—because the liquid is so heavy that it would pull him to the ground as it dropped suddenly to the lower end of the flask.

**Water and Ice.** These most common, most familiar, and most essential substances answer to every definition of a mineral and a rock. They are minerals in the precise sense (see page 2) and when they occur in large bodies they are also rocks, constituting a conspicuous part of the structure of the earth.

Their significance in this respect hardly needs emphasis. Imagine the earth without its vast oceans, even without its lakes and streams! True, our globe has existed in the past without the great glaciers and ice sheets of the polar regions and the high altitudes, but we would scarcely recognize such places as Alaska and Switzerland if all the ice were suddenly to disappear.

When a given volume of water freezes to ice it expands by nearly one tenth, becoming that much lighter and floating on the still-liquid water. This expansion of water is the reverse of almost every other known chemical compound; other fluids shrink when they turn solid and so occupy less space than before.

The importance to our everyday life of this peculiarity of water cannot be overstated. If water freezing at the surface of a lake in winter, for example, contracted and became heavier, it would sink to the bottom, pile up there, and eventually fill the lake. The long interval required to melt it would upset the balance of nature. Instead, the cover of floating ice insulates the rest of the lake water from the cold air and keeps it liquid.

Frozen water in the form of ice or snow is a crystalline solid, having an orderly internal arrangement of its atoms. This is proved by the intricate, symmetrical patterns of snowflakes, which look like delicately crocheted lace. The marvelous beauty to be seen in snowflakes, though noted in early times, was first made widely popular by the pioneer work of Wilson A. Bentley of Jericho, Vermont, who caught them freshly fallen and quickly photographed thousands of them, no two alike, through the microscope.

**Itacolumite—the Rock That Bends.** Firmness and solidity are thought to be the very essence of a rock. This is indeed so, even though we have already learned that large bodies of ice and water are truly rocks in the scientific sense. These substances, however, are not generally regarded as rocks in quite the same way as, for instance, granite and limestone are. And so it is with much curiosity that we observe specimens of a flexible sandstone.

Thin slabs of itacolumite will sag under their own weight and ripple mysteriously as they are bent. When turned over, they bend in the opposite direction.

If stronger and not so friable or crumbly, it would doubtless serve as a delightful flooring material, with enough springiness to make walking a pleasure, but itacolumite has no practical use. It is, nevertheless, an important rock from an economic standpoint, because it is a source of gold and a major source of diamonds in the southern part of the Brazilian state of Minas Geraes. These deposits are geolog-

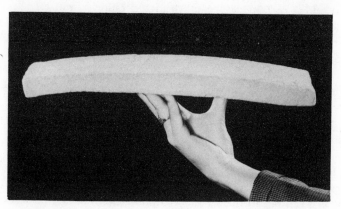

Fig. 35—Itacolumite, or flexible sandstone, bends under its own weight. Slab from Kalyana, India. (*Courtesy of Ward's Natural Science Establishment.*)

ically very ancient, much older than the diamond pipes of Africa. Despite their great age, and although they in turn furnished the gem crystals found in the stream gravels at lower elevations, they are not themselves the original home of the diamonds. This primary source must have been some type of igneous rock, probably similar to the kimberlite of the African pipe mines, described in Chapter 5.

The first recognition of diamonds in Brazil, about 1720, took place at Tejuco, now the thriving city appropriately named Diamantina. The parent rock here is itacolumite, in which the diamond crystals are embedded in clay.

The same kind of rock occurs in India, in the Ural Mountains, and in the southern Appalachians. In all three places diamonds have been found in it. Occasional crystals associated with itacolumite have come from Georgia and North Carolina.

The flexibility of itacolumite seems to be caused by a fortunate combination of conditions. The rock consists mainly of symmetrically arranged quartz grains which interlock, so that, as the specimens are bent, they rotate against one another like the joints in bones. Enough mica is included to add a certain degree of elasticity; chlorite and talc are flexible, micalike minerals also present. Furthermore, itacolumite is somewhat porous, owing presumably to the circulation of underground water through fissures in the rock.

The nature of itacolumite and the alteration which it has undergone cause many petrologists—the scientists who study rocks—to consider a large proportion of it as a metamorphic rock, a kind of quartzite, rather than as sandstone, a sedimentary rock.

**Pumice—a Rock That Floats.** When lava emerges onto the surface of the ground, the pressure upon the molten rock is relieved and the superheated steam contained within it is given off, in the same way that carbon dioxide bubbles out of a bottle of ginger ale when the cap is removed. If the lava is still somewhat mushy, the escaping vapors tend to puff it up into a spongy froth called pumice. This takes place most often in the throat of a volcano or in the top part of the lava flow where the gases expand most rapidly.

Seen with a magnifying lens, pumice appears to be a mass of silky fibers of glass, full of small cells separated by larger pores. These isolated air holes enable pumice to float almost indefinitely on water, so that pieces of it thrown out of volcanoes under water or along the coast are carried long distances by currents, eventually drifting ashore in every part of the world.

Its sharp cutting edges make pumice an excellent abrasive for many purposes, of which the most familiar is dental powder. Good white pumice has long been mined on Lipari, one of the Aeolian Islands off the tip of Sicily. In recent years most of the total production of pumice has been used as an aggregate in concrete for buildings; an outstanding example of such construction is the Los Angeles Telephone Exchange. Pumice for this purpose occurs widely in the western states.

The smaller-grained commercial varieties of pumice are called pumicite. The dark-colored and heavier equivalent of pumice is called scoria. This grades into ordinary basalt (described on page 66), which is frequently characterized by gas pores, either hollow or lined with later minerals.

**Fulgurite—Petrified Lightning.** When lightning strikes a patch of loose sand, it fuses the grains into a narrow hollow tube or pipe of quartz glass which is called a fulgurite. Such tubes may extend downward several inches, or, in unusual examples, a yard or more. They often branch into fantastic shapes as they descend. The thin shells of glass enclose rough pieces of sand that were not affected by the heat, and they also contain many bubbles in spots where moisture in the sand suddenly expanded into steam. Glass threads hang like whiskers from the outside of the tubes. Many fulgurites seem to have been squeezed oval by the surrounding cylinders of sand while they were hot enough to be plastic.

Sand dunes, especially, reveal numerous fulgurites to the

observant collector of such freaks of nature. Although dunes are land forms typical of deserts, they may occur in any climate wherever there are strong winds and dry sand; they migrate constantly until a surface barrier eventually stops them. Sandy coasts facing onshore winds, and rivers with variable flows of water are other favorable places for the accumulation of sand dunes. As a dune shifts ever so slightly, the hard tops of fulgurites may project above the sand.

Another kind of fulgurite, but much less numerous, is formed when lightning hits the bare surface of rocks unprotected by vegetation. This is most apt to occur near the summits of mountains, where terrifying flashes of lightning are frequent. The rocks show the effect of fusion in this manner by a glassy spot or thin crust, resembling a film of varnish. Noticed by the early naturalists among the peaks of central Europe, fulgurites of this variety have been described from many localities. Sometimes lightning seems to have struck a crack in a rock and melted the adjacent material enough to produce a short tubular fulgurite, which may be considered a combination of the two main types, in sand and hard rock, respectively.

**Oil Shale.** The largest mineral deposit in the world, except the ocean itself, is the body of oil shale in northwestern Colorado, northeastern Utah, and southwestern Wyoming, from which a large share of the world's future gasoline and petroleum may come. The amount of recoverable oil is estimated at 100 billion barrels. This great mineral resource is the shale of the Green River formation, deposited sometime from 36 to 56 million years ago in a vast shallow-water interior lake, which has been given the name Lake Uinta.

Judging from the annual deposits known as varves, Lake Uinta must have existed for six and one-half million years before it dried up. Aquatic plants, especially algae, grew in profusion in it. Their waxy, resinous, and fatty remains resisted decay and settled to the bottom, together with the entombed bodies of insects and fish. Some of the choicest specimens of fossil fish come from these sedimentary rocks.

No oil is visible in the shale; in fact, none is actually there, and the exposed rock is almost white. Organic matter is present, however, in a solid form called kerogen, which yields oil when heated to a high temperature in special furnaces. This process is called destructive distillation. The United States Bureau of Mines has developed methods for mining the shale at a remarkably low cost and for extracting the oil at a price that will eventually enable it to compete with petroleum pumped from wells.

The richest beds are about 70 feet thick. The country here is rugged, with cliffs of tough shale rearing a sheer 3,000 feet above the Colorado River. Trucks haul the broken rock from the mine to the experimental plant over a breathtaking road which snakes precariously across the side of the canyon.

We have here a curious rock indeed—a hard rock which gives up a golden liquid, someday to fuel our vehicles and machinery, to wage war or enrich peace.

Oil shale in Scotland was, interestingly enough, exploited profitably a century ago, until crude petroleum was brought into Britain from the rich fields of the Near East. The oil shale industry in France is even older, dating from 1830. Other deposits of lower-grade oil shale are situated in Canada, parts of the United States, and several other nations.

**Bentonite.** Because it absorbs moisture, bentonite swells when submerged in water, taking up as much as five times its own weight and enlarging as much as fifty times its previous volume. This expansion enables bentonite to be used for many industrial purposes. It holds molding sand together, it filters and purifies numerous commercial products, and it fills the pores in rocks being drilled for oil wells, as well as serving to bring the broken rock fragments out of the hole. There are a hundred other uses for bentonite.

The principal constituent of bentonite is a clay mineral called montmorillonite, which makes it soft and slippery to the touch. Originally volcanic ash blown out of a crater, transported by wind, and deposited in water, bentonite is now the altered residue of such material. It makes up thin beds which uniformly cover a considerable area.

South Dakota and Wyoming are the leading producers of superior bentonite from the Black Hills region. The appearance of beds of bentonite as they outcrop at the surface is distinctive; they support vegetation but feebly, and their barren wrinkled look causes them to resemble reefs of coral. The beds are mined at shallow depths with mechanical shovels.

**Loess.** "More and more of less and less" could be a description of the way in which a combination of volcanic ash, wind-blown dust, stream silt, and glacial clay piles up to build a deposit of the strange rock known as loess. This German word, which only a German-speaking person can say properly, is getting to be pronounced simply to rhyme with "guess." Not inappropriately either—for the origin and source of the material that goes by this name have for a long time confounded students of the earth sciences.

Some have ascribed the origin of loess to volcanic explosions, others to the grinding action of glaciers, some to deposition on the floodplains of streams, and still others to the wind. The most likely origin seems to be as a wind-blown deposit of desert dust or glacial rock powder. Loess perhaps as thick as a thousand feet, covering a tremendous area in north-central China, has come from the Gobi and other deserts in the arid interior. Large parts of more than a dozen states in the Mississippi Valley are covered with loess apparently derived from the fine rock flour that was pulverized by the mighty glaciers of the Ice Age. Loess is also widespread in the pampas of Argentina and the plains of Germany.

The notable characteristic of loess is its tendency to stand up as steep cliffs, in spite of its being a soft and porous material. Deep, narrow gorges, which serve as the main highways in remote parts of China, have been incised into deposits of loess by the tread of countless people and animals during past centuries. High cliffs of loess along the Missouri River afforded valuable observation posts to Indians, scouts, and settlers in the early days of the West; Council Bluffs in Iowa is such a cliff.

The visible means of support to which loess owes its upright position in the world of rocks is an abundance of slender vertical calcite-encrusted tubes. These represent the roots and stems of successive generations of grass and moss which grew in the loess and were smothered under fresh layers of the powdery material. Hence loess erodes into roughly vertical columns, even though the horizontal stratification typical of most sedimentary rocks is lacking.

Under a microscope, samples of loess reveal its constituents to be sharp grains of numerous common minerals (chiefly quartz) mixed with clay and only partly cemented by calcium carbonate. The shells of snails and the bones of other land animals are frequent, as are oddly shaped concretions.

The most fertile soil in China, and equally so in the corn belt of Iowa and Illinois, comes from the loess that blankets the countryside. Caves dug by hand into the soft rock of the cliffs furnish shelter for many a Chinese farmer. The Yellow River and the Yellow Sea get their names from the color imparted to them by the enormous quantities of loess they receive from the eroded land.

# 16

# Man-made Minerals

The first scientific experiments in making synthetic minerals were designed to duplicate in the laboratory the conditions existing in nature, in order to learn more about the temperature, pressure, and other factors that may be involved.

These early attempts were necessarily crude, but with improved techniques came the desire to make artificial minerals in quantities sufficient to be used for industrial and military purposes.

The newest of these synthetic minerals is a variation of muscovite, the white mica so vital in electrical equipment. Research scientists at the Electrochemical Laboratory of the United States Bureau of Mines at Norris, Tennessee, have succeeded in the large-scale production of a fluorine-bearing phlogopite mica that is even better in resisting breakdown at high temperatures than the natural material. Such success promises to make this country entirely independent of foreign sources for this strategic mineral, which has hitherto come largely from India and Brazil. The dry oxides from three common earth materials—glass sand, bauxite, and magnesite—and a potassium silicofluoride (which is obtained as a by-product of the phosphate-fertilizer industry and which acts as a crystallizing agent) are placed together in a silicon carbide crucible and melted in an electric furnace.

Applying an alternating current of electricity to plates of quartz, properly oriented and cut to the right thickness, causes them to change volume so rapidly that they vibrate at high frequency. When the current corresponds to the natural frequency of the quartz, this vibration is greatly magnified. Such quartz wafers are employed to maintain the wave length of radio broadcasts and to control the frequency in telephone communication and radar. Until it becomes feasible to apply to timekeeping the precise rate of rotation of electrons in the ammonium or cesium atom, the accuracy of the finest master clocks in the United States Bureau of Standards will be obtained by using the frequency of quartz oscillating 100,000 times a second. Inasmuch as natural quartz for these purposes must be free from internal twinning and other defects, and suitable crystals, which come almost entirely from Brazil, were getting scarce, the preparation of synthetic quartz was encouraged and made possible as a national defense measure.

An even newer substitute for synthetic quartz is ethylene diamine tartrate, known as E.D.T., which is an organic substance grown in large crystals by the Bell Telephone Company laboratories. A companion crystal, also used in telephone communication, is D.K.T., dipotassium tartrate.

Other synthetic crystals besides E.D.T. and D.K.T. are available commercially, but, unlike quartz, none of these is found in nature as a mineral. The earliest of them was rochelle salt, used mainly as a phonograph pickup to create coherent sound from the varying pressure of a phonograph needle. Developed and widely exploited during the Second World War, ammonium dihydrogen phosphate (A.D.P.) largely replaced rochelle salt in the uses of underwater sound, particularly submarine detection by the sonar method. A number of artificial crystals have proved able to serve as detectors of nuclear radiation, substituting for Geiger counters, as described on page 156.

Fluorescent minerals are synthesized for use in television screens and in the lighting tubes now so familiar everywhere as sources of illumination. Willemite made fluorescent by manganese, and sphalerite and greenockite activated by copper and silver are produced commercially for these purposes.

The ceramic industries utilize various minerals of synthetic origin. These include corundum, cordierite, enstatite, and forsterite. Cristobalite is made on a large scale by converting quartz into its high-temperature equivalent. Mullite, though rare as a natural mineral, has long been produced artificially by heating sillimanite, andalusite, kyanite, or dumortierite; the resulting mixture of mullite and a siliceous glass serves as an excellent heat- and shock-resisting substance in spark plugs, porcelain, and enamelware. The newest ceramic is hot-pressed synthetic mica of the fluor-phlogopite type already mentioned, the binding agent being phosphoric acid.

The consumers' demand for greater uniformity of color, together with the approaching depletion of natural deposits, has forced the pigment industry to turn its attention to synthetic coloring materials. The iron pigments known as ocher, umber, and sienna have largely been replaced by their synthetic counterparts. Synthetic ultramarine has been made for over a century as a substitute for the rich blue pigment formerly extracted from lapis lazuli and highly valued by artists, especially in the Middle Ages. Rutile and anatase (both titanium oxides), crocoite (lead chromate), and greenockite (cadmium sulfide) are among the numerous other minerals that are now being made artificially for pigments. Further experimentation is proceeding at a rapid pace in this industry.

Because of their high value, gem minerals were the first to be produced synthetically in any considerable amount. As with the other minerals already mentioned, these synthetic gems have the same chemical composition and atomic structure as the natural ones for which they substitute. Where others had failed, August Verneuil, a French chemist, succeeded in 1902 in producing synthetic corundum in the form of synthetic ruby of admirable beauty, perfection, and size. Synthetic blue sapphire was created in 1910, and since then synthetic corundum has been marketed in a wide array of superb colors. Star ruby and star sapphire were produced synthetically in commercial quantity in 1947 by the Linde Company.

A modified version of Verneuil's original equipment, consisting of a furnace with an inverted oxygen-hydrogen blow-pipe, is still used. Powdered aluminum oxide, ground impalpably fine and mixed with the proper coloring agent, is tapped through a screen, past which it drifts down a tube of oxygen. A jet of hydrogen entering from the side joins the oxygen to fire a flame of over 3,750 degrees Fahrenheit. This temperature is sufficient to melt the powder, which drops onto a rotating pedestal and builds up into a pear-shaped crystal called a boule. A wartime development was the manufacture of corundum in long slender rods, eliminating several steps in the manufacture of bearings. One should, of course, realize that the technological applications of these synthetic gems are far more important than their use in jewelry. Textile thread-guides, oil-burner nozzles, gauges, vacuum thermionic devices, electric-meter bearings—these are only a few of the multitude of uses for synthetic corundum. The material for such purposes is largely of the colorless variety known in gemology as synthetic white sapphire—the absence of color has no influence on the hardness of the gem.

While attempting to secure the elusive blue color in synthetic corundum, which is aluminum oxide, magnesium oxide was added as a flux. The resulting stone proved instead to be a different species, corresponding in composition to spinel, which may be regarded as a multiple oxide of magnesium and aluminum. This accidental product is now made in numerous colors and is sold as a substitute for other gems having names that are more familiar to the general public than spinel. Most so-called "synthetic zircon," for example, is really synthetic spinel colored greenish blue by cobalt oxide. The same is true of the lighter-colored "synthetic aquamarine."

Synthetic emerald is a more recent addition to the slowly increasing number of artificial gems. The difficulty of making this variety of beryl in large enough sizes has retarded its sale, but future advances in manufacture seem certain. Carroll F. Chatham of San Francisco is the sole American producer of synthetic emerald, following in the path of German pioneers who turned out these crystals as long ago as 1912.

Synthetic gems can be recognized by the trained gemologist, although some of the more deceptive stones defy all but a few experts. The internal markings and inclusions furnish the usual clue to their identity. These consist of round and oval gas bubbles from the furnace instead of actual foreign crystals of natural origin; curved instead of straight color-bands and structure-lines; and undissolved clots of the added coloring matter.

A gem that does not need such careful scrutiny is synthetic rutile, sold mostly under the name titania because it consists of titanium oxide. This achievement of science can scarcely be regarded as a mere substitute, because natural rutile is not known in gem-quality crystals large enough to cut, its usual occurrence as a gem being needlelike inclusions in quartz (see page 112). Titania amazingly outsparkles even diamond, although it is nowhere near so hard. A related substance, strontium titanate, quite unknown as a mineral, is the latest synthetic gem to appear on the market.

Until 1954 synthetic diamond remained the one great challenge to the maker of crystals. Its conquest by scientists of the General Electric Research Laboratory in Schenectady, New York, is a triumph of extraordinary magnitude, not only for its theoretical significance but because industry will benefit immeasurably by having an unlimited supply of its best abrasive. Diamond is deceptive in its simplicity, being composed of a single chemical element, carbon; nevertheless, that one constituent had previously defied the most strenuous efforts of crystallographers to reproduce it in the required form. The new process involves a temperature above 5,000 degrees and a pressure equivalent to that existing 240 miles below the surface of the earth. Henri Moissan, a French chemist and Nobel prize winner in 1906, and J. B. Hannay, a nineteenth-century British chemist, had both been credited with making tiny diamonds on an experimental basis, but no incontrovertible proof exists today that either of them was actually successful.

# 17

# Your Rock and Mineral Collection

The mineral kingdom is as near as your garden soil and as broad as the universe. The collector of rocks and minerals may, within these pretty wide limits, adjust his activities to the time, energy, and money available to him for this particular pursuit.

Making a comprehensive general collection is rarely attempted or desired; this task is better left to the large museums of science or natural history. The preferred way to collect is to specialize—even while saving a little room for the secret loves, those extra specimens that may not fit into the category selected but which are just too attractive or interesting to be disposed of.

As with rare books, antiques, or other objects, the earth materials to be collected should always be those that arouse your greatest enthusiasm. Such specialization will furnish the maximum satisfaction; if, furthermore, the specimens are carefully selected, you will have a really valuable collection. Each of the varied products of the mineral kingdom—rocks, minerals, ores, metals, crystals, gems, or meteorites—can make a worthwhile display. Even some of these require further breakdown by subject to keep them from becoming too unwieldy or expensive.

A mineral collection, for example, may perhaps be grouped according to one of the following considerations: industrial use (as abrasive or gem); chief metal (as copper or zinc); chief chemical element (as barium or calcium); geologic occurrence (as ore, vein, or placer deposit); geologic origin (as igneous, sedimentary, or metamorphic); geographic occurrence (by continent, country, state, county, or other area); crystallization (as twin crystals or by crystal system); optical property (as color or luster); physical property (as habit or specific gravity); or individual species (as a specialized collection of quartz or calcite).

Rocks, which are more difficult to identify than minerals, are also harder to classify. Chapter 6 presents a simplified field classification suitable for a general rock collection. Separate classifications have been published in various books for highly specialized collections of meteorites and other objects that also belong to the mineral kingdom.

The size of the specimens as well as their number is almost always an urgent consideration. If you have unlimited room you might gather large specimens, but only if you can afford the showy, museum type of material, or else you will acquire worthless rock in bulk. Other collectors must of necessity limit their acquisitions to hand-sized pieces or to the still-smaller thumbnail specimens, which grade downward into micromounts—tiny crystals mounted in a box and viewed under magnification. These exquisite miniatures, revealing a veritable fairyland of color and form, usually require the use of a microscope and some experience in selecting minerals.

## HOW TO SECURE SPECIMENS

Rocks and minerals are to be found almost everywhere, even if occurring only as small pebbles in the garden soil. Certain places are, of course, more favorable than others, and it is to such places that the collector directs his attention.

Beach sands often yield a surprising number of minerals, because they have come from many sources, though most of them are of the usual size of sand, too small to be preserved as individual specimens. Mixed with them will be larger pebbles, mostly quartz. Desert sands may be less varied, but they may have rare minerals of outstanding interest. Some collectors specialize in bottles of sand samples.

Playa lakes are temporary bodies of water situated in basins in dry regions—they expand, contract, and even disappear according to the season. They are numerous in California, Nevada, Utah, and other western states. Upon drying up, the playa lakes deposit crystals of common salt and other saline compounds, including sulfate and borate minerals. The wind at times blows mineral-laden water against obstructions and the crystals may continue to grow to considerable dimensions.

The gas cavities in the rock of lava flows frequently contain linings of agate, crystals of quartz, and many other results of late mineral deposition. Calcite and the zeolites are among the most abundant minerals having this type of occurrence so prominent in Hawaii and elsewhere.

Hot springs are a likely place to look for minerals and rocks. The porous carbonate rock called travertine is especially familiar in such an environment. The springs may have ceased to function long ago but their former presence is revealed by their deposits.

Banks or pits of gravel, sand, and clay usually contain specimens of miscellaneous rocks and minerals scattered about indiscriminately. Among them may be found really worthwhile crystals or clusters of minerals, such as those of pyrite, marcasite, and gypsum which are native to clay beds.

Open cuts and excavations made for commercial purposes should be examined. These include foundations of buildings, road and railway cuts, and tunnels. Man-made openings for the express purpose of extracting rock and mineral products are known as quarries and mines. They are the chief sources of mineral and rock specimens. Prosaic as they sound, coal mines, with their ample evidences of prehistoric plant life, are interesting places. Admittance to operating quarries can usually be secured, but most mines are dangerous, and abandoned ones should be avoided by inexperienced collectors.

The heaps of waste rock around a mine or quarry, called dumps, are always worth an inspection. Sometimes, good specimens can be obtained by digging. Those samples that are damaged or weathered at least indicate what sort of material has come from the deposit.

Attractive pieces of discarded stone can be had at monument works, especially at establishments that trim and polish their own rock.

Even where no actual mining has been done, the presence of a prominently exposed cliff or an outcrop of rock different from the normal kind in a given locality should tempt the mineral collector until he investigates its possibilities. Cavities or "pockets" are the best spots in which to find crystals, because the available space has given them a chance to develop without hindrance.

The accidental discoveries of specimens in unexpected places have been too many to relate. As you might suppose, however, these "accidents" seem to happen most frequently to the observant collector who has become acquainted, Indian-fashion, with the signs of nature that point to the presence of "game."

To accompany an organized field trip to a well-established locality is often the best way to start collecting, because it furnishes the company of others who may have a good deal of knowledge to impart in addition to their companionship. Field trips are one of the major activities of most mineral clubs and societies that have been formed in practically every state and province in the United States and Canada. Besides trips for the purpose of prospecting and collecting, these groups hold indoor meetings and participate—often through the regional federations—in conventions which feature exhibits on a large scale.

Museums are another place to see typical as well as spectacular specimens, and the labels may suggest localities for your own expeditions. Colleges and universities also maintain collections of rocks and minerals in their geological departments, if not in separate museums. In the western mining country, specimens from nearby mines are often displayed in county courthouses and assayers' shops, and indicate what might be available in the vicinity.

Most collectors of rocks and minerals trade specimens as eagerly as do those in other hobbies—another advantage in belonging to a mineral society. Trading at a distance may be disappointing because crystallized minerals are apt to be seriously damaged in shipment unless care is taken in packing them, but otherwise this can be a satisfying way of building a collection.

Purchasing specimens is recommended because few collectors can hope personally to secure a wide enough variety by finding or trading them. Dealers are now established in many towns; their advertisements appear in the mineral magazines named on page 241. Inexpensive samples of the more common minerals and rocks are useful in learning to recognize and test them. Being familiar, for instance, with the characteristic appearance of feldspar, quartz, mica, and hornblende in good-sized pieces bought for a few cents from a mineral dealer will aid vastly in the quick recognition of the same minerals when they are seen in small grains in a normal granite.

You might wish to grow your own crystals. Little space is required and there are countless combinations to reward the patient crystalmaker. Saturated solutions of certain chemicals tend to develop attractive forms and pretty colors with a minimum of attention. Sodium chloride, copper sulfate, and potassium alum are among the substances that can be produced readily in a covered Mason jar. The procedure is described in several recent books (see page 244). Varying the temperature and adding certain impurities will cause surprising changes in the size and shape of the crystal, corresponding to the diversity of habit which is characteristic of natural crystals.

The beginning mineral and rock collector should own a few of the basic books on geology and mineralogy listed on page 242 and read one of the magazines devoted to his hobby. Later he may benefit from the more professional and technical journals. Publications of the national, state, and provincial geologic surveys are valuable aids in finding localities and learning about them. Government maps are an essential part of the collector's equipment and they can be bought at low prices.

## EQUIPMENT AND CARE

Once in the field a rock and mineral collector realizes that his most essential piece of equipment is a suitable hammer. Prospector's or geologist's hammers have a sharp pick or flat chisel on the opposite side. If the pick edge is preferred, a separate cold chisel will often be found useful. Several weights of hammers, with wood or steel handles, are available, including sledges which are useful but too heavy to carry far. With ingenuity a number of stone cutter's, carpenter's, and dentist's tools—depending upon the delicacy of the work—can be adapted to removing and trimming specimens. The initial task of trimming should be done on the spot to reduce the amount of waste rock carried home. At the same time the poorer grade of specimen should be discarded entirely.

A knapsack of leather, canvas, or cloth serves as a collecting bag as well as for carrying small tools and personal items. Separate bags of cloth or paper will hold the individual specimens, which should be amply wrapped in cotton, tissue paper, or newspaper, according to their fragility. Crystals must always be treated with care. A label should be wrapped with each specimen in order to identify its source. A convenient way to apply a temporary label is by means of a strip of adhesive tape, previously numbered and notched for easy removal and kept fresh by attaching it to a sheet of plastic. Above all, a notebook should be taken to record the data otherwise difficult to remember; it will prove of increasing interest as the years pass.

Each collector will have his own choice as to any additional equipment that may be wanted. Appropriate clothing is required for comfort against the weather and protection against hazards to be encountered, ranging from snake bite to flying chips of rock. A camera, magnifying glass, pocket-knife, pencil, field book, locality guide, maps—almost everyone uses some of these while collecting, in addition to the sort of equipment normally associated with camping and other outdoor activities.

**Trimming.** Although most of the rough shaping of specimens ought to be done at the locality, most specimens will be improved by trimming them further at home. An exception to removing the surrounding rock is preferably made when dealing with the acceptable matrix that accompanies a crystal and adds to its value because it proves what the original rock associations were. A cluster of green tourmaline crystals in dolomite from Campolongo, Switzerland, for example, is of more interest and value than the loose crystals would be. Rock specimens are customarily trimmed to a pillow shape, about 3 x 4 x 1 inches or slightly larger, called hand specimens. You may want your own specimens to be much smaller.

**Cleaning.** Attractive minerals are clean minerals. As with the human skin, the application of ordinary soap and water is best for all minerals except the unusually delicate and sensitive ones. A detergent can be substituted to advantage since it leaves less film, though rinsing should be a general rule. Firm specimens will stand scrubbing with a stiff brush, and occasionally even a wire brush is needed, as well as special acid treatments in stubborn cases. Hot water can damage a few minerals; native sulfur may likewise crack in water that is too cold; and certain minerals, the most familiar of which is halite, are soluble in any water, so that cleaning fluid or alcohol needs to be applied. Among the other common minerals that seem to be injured by moisture are pyrite and marcasite—these iron sulfides are notoriously troublesome. Earthy substances such as clay are likewise difficult to wash. Air blown from a syringe and the judicious use of a soft brush will improve the appearance of delicate minerals, including even those that develop the intricately grown fibrous and needlelike crystals which break so readily.

**Labeling.** To the experienced collector of earth substances, any specimen that lacks an identifying label, no matter how excellent it might be otherwise, is little better than "just a rock" and has but slight value. The really essential part of the label is not the name of the specimen, for that may be determined by examining and testing it, but the locality information, telling as closely as possible where the specimen was found. Permanent labels may be made by lettering or typing on adhesive tape or writing in India ink on a spot of white ink or enamel. Accession numbers, running consecutively from 1, may be placed on the specimens, and the corresponding numbers, together with full descriptions, should be filed on separate index cards or loose-leaf sheets.

**Display.** The preparation of a display of rock and mineral specimens allows as wide a latitude for the private tastes and pocketbook of the individual collector as the acquisition of the specimens themselves—from simple storage boxes to expensive cases of the kind installed in public museums. Bookcases, china cabinets, and chests of drawers are probably the most common articles of furniture used to house collections. Homemade shelving is often encountered, as are portable cases which can be dismounted for exhibition at shows and lectures. Many collectors like to mount their specimens on small stands of plastic or wood which bear attached labels. The lighting fixtures vary from strings of Christmas-tree bulbs to fluorescent tubes. The skillful installation of mirrors magnifies the size of a display and increases the brilliant reflections. Frames to hang like pictures serve well to exhibit small specimens; such a standard holder is the paper-bound and glass-topped *Riker mount*. Sands are generally kept in inverted jars of uniform size and shape. Whatever the method employed to display them, all the specimens on display should be neatly trimmed and cleaned,

then kept clean; they should also be clearly labeled to avoid
the necessity of explaining every specimen to visitors, aes-
thetically arranged without crowding and with some sem-
blance of systematic order, and adequately lighted. Good
housekeeping is a sign of the veteran collector and it can
be tried to advantage by the novice.

**Preservation.** Surely as much thought should be given
to caring for specimens after they have been acquired as
was devoted to obtaining them. Some minerals are not stable
under ordinary conditions, and even those that are stable
may be made less attractive by dust, scratches, or cracks.

The change that minerals undergo after they have been
removed from the earth, their natural home, is the result of
their adjustment to a new environment to which, like living
organisms, they are responsive. An extreme instance of such
a change is the crumbling of a meteorite to powder in a
museum collection, clearly suggesting that the environment
of the earth's atmosphere must be very different from that
of the outer space from which meteorites come.

Delicate specimens, such as zeolite needles, should be enclosed to protect them from dust and other dirt, since they
are not easy to clean. Minerals that tarnish, such as native
silver, or those that oxidize, especially pyrite and marcasite,
may be preserved by coating them with any of the commercial transparent lacquers. Light-sensitive minerals, such as
realgar and certain silver ores, should be kept in the dark,
lest they change color. Minerals that absorb moisture and
tend to dissolve, as halite, or lose water and fall to pieces,
as borax, need to be bottled away from excessively moist or
dry air. Abrupt changes of temperature and, of course, care-
less handling are eternal enemies of minerals.

# Magazines and Books

The following magazines are national publications on a popular level and are devoted to the subjects covered in this book. In addition there are various regional periodicals and a large number of trade and technical journals which may be consulted in public libraries.

*Earth Science.* Edited by Dr. Ben H. Wilson, it includes worthwhile articles on rocks, minerals, and popular geology. It is published bimonthly at Box 1357, Chicago 90, Illinois; the subscription price is $2.50 per year.

*Rocks and Minerals.* Edited since 1926 by Peter Zodac, it covers the entire field of minerals and rocks. It is published bimonthly at Box 29, Peekskill, New York; the subscription price is $3.00 per year.

*Gems and Minerals.* Edited by Don MacLachlan, it has short illustrated articles and current news on the various phases of the mineral hobby. It is published monthly at Box 687, Mentone, California; the subscription price is $3.00 per year.

*The Mineralogist.* Edited by Don MacLachlan, it deals interestingly with all aspects of the mineral hobby. It is published bimonthly at Box 808, Mentone, California; the subscription price is $2.00 per year.

*The Lapidary Journal.* Edited by Hugh Leiper, it specializes in the collecting and cutting of gems and ornamental stones. It is published monthly at Box 2369, San Diego 12, California; the subscription price is $4.50 per year.

*Desert.* Edited by Eugene L. Conrotto, it features articles on geologic subjects and mineral localities in southwestern United States, illustrated with helpful maps. It is published monthly at Palm Desert, California; the subscription price is $4.00 per year.

*The Mining Record.* Edited by Herchal C. Helm, it deals with prospecting and western mining. It is published weekly at 1950 Curtis Street, Denver 2, Colorado; the subscription price is $6.00 per year.

## RECOMMENDED READING

More specialized and extensive information about subjects discussed in this book will be found in the following volumes, which have been selected as most suitable for nonspecialist readers.

### Mineral Collecting

*How to Know the Minerals and Rocks* by Richard M. Pearl, published in 1955 by McGraw-Hill Book Company, Inc., New York. A practical field guide to more than 125 important minerals and rocks, featuring basic keys for identifying typical specimens without special skill or equipment; includes many marked drawings and color plates.

*Ultraviolet Guide to Minerals* by Sterling Gleason, published in 1960 by D. Van Nostrand Company, Inc., New York. Prospecting for and collecting fluorescent minerals.

*Gem Hunter's Guide* by Russell P. MacFall, 3d edition published in 1963 by Thomas Y. Crowell, New York. Interesting aspects of mineral collecting and a detailed listing of United States mineral localities.

*Gemstones and Minerals: How and Where to Find Them* by John Sinkankas, published in 1961 by D. Van Nostrand Company, Inc., New York. A general, well-illustrated book on mineral and gem collecting and localities.

(See also Richard M. Pearl, *Successful Mineral Collecting and Prospecting.*)

### Mineral Identification

*Identification and Qualitative Chemical Analysis of Minerals* by Orsino C. Smith, published (2d edition) in 1953 by

D. Van Nostrand Company, Inc., New York. This reference book covers the detailed testing and laboratory identification of minerals, with extensive tables of properties and color plates.

*The Mineral Key* by Howard B. Graves, Jr., published in 1947 by McGraw-Hill Book Company, Inc., New York. An outline for the simple identification of minerals.

(See also Richard M. Pearl, *How to Know the Minerals and Rocks* [a field guide] and college textbooks on minerals by Cornelius S. Hurlbut, Austin F. Rogers, Alexander N. Winchell, and Edward H. Kraus.)

## Minerals

*1001 Questions Answered about the Mineral Kingdom* by Richard M. Pearl, published in 1959 by Dodd, Mead and Company, New York. Full answers to more than a thousand questions often asked about major branches of the mineral kingdom.

*Getting Acquainted with Minerals* by George L. English and David E. Jensen, 2d edition published in 1958 by McGraw-Hill Book Company, Inc., New York. This is a well illustrated introductory book which includes discussions of mineral properties, descriptions of minerals, and information for collectors.

*Minerals and How to Study Them* by Edward S. Dana and Cornelius S. Hurlbut, Jr., published (3d edition) in 1949 by John Wiley and Sons, Inc., New York. This is an elementary textbook which describes mineral properties, and provides descriptions of minerals and information on growing crystals.

(See also Russell D. George, *Minerals and Rocks*.)

NOTE:
The following books are college textbooks on the science of mineralogy, including crystallography and mineral identification.

*Dana's Manual of Mineralogy,* 17th edition revised by Cornelius S. Hurlbut, Jr., published in 1959 by John Wiley and Sons, Inc., New York.

*Introduction to the Study of Minerals* by Austin F. Rogers, published (3d edition) in 1937 by McGraw-Hill Book Company, Inc., New York.

*Elements of Mineralogy* by Alexander N. Winchell, published in 1942 by Prentice-Hall, Inc., New York.

*Mineralogy* by Edward H. Kraus, Walter F. Hunt, and Lewis S. Ramsdell, published (5th edition) in 1959 by McGraw-Hill Book Company, Inc., New York.

*Principles of Mineralogy* by William H. Dennen, published in 1959 by Ronald Press Company, New York.

*Elements of Crystallography and Mineralogy* by F. Alton Wade and Richard B. Mattox, published in 1960 by Harper and Brothers, New York.

*Mineralogy* by Leonard Berry and Brian Mason, published in 1959 by W. H. Freeman and Company, San Francisco.

### Rocks

*Minerals and Rocks* by Russell D. George, published in 1943 by Appleton-Century-Crofts, Inc., New York. A comprehensive book on rocks and their minerals.

*Guide to the Study of Rocks* by L. E. Spock, published (2d edition) in 1962 by Harper and Brothers, New York. A textbook on the principal rocks of all types.

*Rocks and Rock Minerals* by Louis V. Pirsson and Adolph Knopf, published (3d edition) in 1947 by John Wiley and Sons, New York. A general textbook on igneous, sedimentary, and metamorphic rocks.

*Kemp's Handbook of Rocks* by Frank F. Grout, published (6th edition) in 1940 by D. Van Nostrand Company, Inc., New York. An introductory textbook on the various kinds of rocks.

### Meteorites

*Out of the Sky: An Introduction to Meteoritics* by Harvey H. Nininger, republished in 1959 by Dover Publications, Inc., New York. A comprehensive survey of meteorite minerals, structures, falls, craters, and all other aspects of this science.

*Meteorites* by Brian Mason, published in 1962 by John Wiley and Sons, Inc., New York.

## Gems

*Popular Gemology* by Richard M. Pearl, republished (2d edition) in 1958 by Sage Books, Denver. This well illustrated book surveys in layman's language the modern knowledge about gems, with information about localities, production, cutting, uses, and identification.

*The Story of the Gems* by Herbert P. Whitlock, republished in 1941 by Emerson Books, Inc., New York. An introductory book, dealing mostly with the lore of gems; finely illustrated.

*A Key to Precious Stones* by L. J. Spencer, republished (2d edition) in 1947 by Emerson Books, Inc., New York. A general introduction to gems, describing them and giving their occurrence.

*Gems and Gem Materials* by Edward H. Kraus and Chester B. Slawson, published (5th edition) in 1947 by McGraw-Hill Book Company, Inc., New York. A college textbook on the principles of gemology, with descriptions of gems and identification tables.

*Gemstones* by G. F. Herbert Smith, 14th edition revised by F. C. Phillips, republished in 1959 by Pitman Publishing Corporation, New York. A comprehensive technical treatise on gems and gemology, with color plates and an extensive bibliography.

*Gems: Their Sources, Descriptions, and Identification* by Robert Webster, published in 1962 by Butterworth's, London. A two-volume, well-illustrated work on gems.

NOTE:
The following books are systematic treatments of gem identification.

*Handbook of Gem Identification* by Richard T. Liddicoat, Jr., published (6th edition) in 1962 by Gemological Institute of America, Los Angeles.

*Gem Testing* by B. W. Anderson, republished (6th edition) in 1959 by Emerson Books, Inc., New York.

The following books describe gem deposits in North America.

*American Gem Trails* by Richard M. Pearl, published in 1964 by McGraw-Hill Book Company, Inc., New York. A reading guide to the gem deposits of the fifty states.

*Gemstones of North America* by John Sinkankas, published in 1959 by D. Van Nostrand Company, Inc., Princeton, New Jersey. An extensive work on gem deposits of the continent.

### Radioactive Minerals

*Minerals for Atomic Energy* by Robert D. Nininger, published (2d edition) in 1956 by D. Van Nostrand Company, Inc., New York. An elementary but comprehensive coverage of uranium, thorium, and beryllium minerals and deposits, from exploration to sale.

*The Uranium and Fluorescent Minerals* by H. C. Dake, published in 1954, distributed by *Gems and Minerals* (magazine), Mentone, California. This book deals with the finding, detection, and description of radioactive minerals, and includes a discussion of luminescent gems and minerals.

### Prospecting

*Handbook for Prospectors and Operators of Small Mines* by Max W. Von Bernewitz, 4th edition revised by Harry C. Chellson, published in 1943 by McGraw-Hill Book Company, Inc., New York. An extensive treatise on the techniques of prospecting and the equipment used.

*Successful Mineral Collecting and Prospecting* by Richard M. Pearl, published in 1961 by McGraw-Hill Book Company, Inc., New York. This book combines both the commercial and hobby aspects of mineral finding.

(See also books on radioactive minerals by Robert D. Nininger and H. C. Dake.)

## Mineral Resources

*Our Mineral Resources* by Charles M. Riley, published in 1959 by John Wiley and Sons, Inc., New York. An elementary textbook on economic geology, covering principles and descriptions of metallic and nonmetallic mineral deposits.

*Minerals in World Industry* by Walter H. Voskuil, published in 1955 by McGraw-Hill Book Company, Inc., New York. This book deals with the international distribution of minerals in relationship to world economy.

*Minerals in World Affairs* by Thomas S. Lovering, published in 1943 by Prentice-Hall, Inc., New York. This book surveys the uses of mineral resources in international affairs, industry, and war.

## Geology

*1001 Questions Answered about Earth Science* by Richard M. Pearl, published in 1962 by Dodd, Mead and Company, New York. A survey of physical and historical geology in question-and-answer style.

*A Textbook of Geomorphology* by Philip G. Worcester, 2d edition published in 1948 by D. Van Nostrand Company, Inc., New York. A general textbook on geology from the standpoint of land forms.

*Geology: An Introduction to Principles of Physical and Historical Geology* by Richard M. Pearl, published (3d edition) in 1963 by Barnes and Noble, Inc., New York. (College Outline Series) A general book for layman and student.

NOTE:

The following are up-to-date standard college textbooks dealing with both physical and historical geology on a suitable level.

*Introduction to Geology* by E. B. Branson and W. A.
    Tarr, 3d edition revised by Carl C. Branson and W. D.

Keller, published in 1952 by McGraw-Hill Book Company, Inc., New York.

*Introduction to Geology* by Howard E. Brown, Victor E. Monnett, and J. Willis Stovall, published in 1958 by Ginn and Company, New York.

*Introduction to College Geology* by Chauncey D. Holmes, published (2d edition) in 1962 by The Macmillan Company,'New York.

*Geology and Man* by Kenneth K. Landes and Russell C. Hussey, published in 1948 by Prentice-Hall, Inc., New York.

*Fundamentals of Earth Science* by Henry D. Thompson, 2d edition published in 1960 by Appleton-Century-Crofts, Inc., New York.

*Elements of Geology* by James H. Zumberge, published (2d edition) in 1963 by John Wiley and Sons, Inc., New York.

# Glossary

**Abrasive:** rock or mineral used to cut and polish industrial material.

**Accession number:** order in which specimen is acquired.

**Acicular habit:** needle-shaped mineral.

**Acid phosphate:** sulfuric-acid-treated phosphate rock used as fertilizer.

**Acidic rock:** silicic rock, having high content of silica.

**Activator:** impurity causing luminescence.

**Adamantine luster:** diamondlike luster of a mineral.

**Alloy:** mixture of metals.

**Alpha ray:** helium atom without electrons.

**Amalgamation:** recovery of gold or silver by use of mercury.

**Ammonium dihydrogen phosphate:** A.D.P., synthetic crystal used in underwater sound.

**Amorphous:** noncrystalline.

**Angstrom unit:** one hundred-millionth of a centimeter.

**Aphanitic texture:** fine-grained texture of igneous rocks.

**Arborescent habit:** flattened fern-shaped growth of manganese or iron oxide.

**Arenaceous rock:** rock containing sand.

**Argon bulb:** source of long-wave ultraviolet light.

**Arsenate:** mineral composed of arsenic, oxygen, and other elements.

**Asphalt:** plastic hydrocarbon formed by evaporation of petroleum.

**Assay wall:** mineralized rock surrounding vein.

**Asterism:** starlike pattern in a mineral.

**Asteroid:** small planet in solar system.

**Atom:** the smallest particle of any chemical element.

**Atomic number:** number of protons or electrons in an atom.

**Atomic weight:** sum of the weights of the protons and neutrons in an atomic nucleus.

**Axis:** direction in a crystal.

**Background count:** impulses produced in Geiger counter by cosmic rays.

**Base metal:** common metal, excluding iron and its alloys.

**Basic rock:** rock having high content of iron and magnesium, low silica content.

**Beta ray:** electron.

**Biogenic rock:** rock formed by organic action.

**Black light:** ultraviolet radiation.

**Black sand:** sand containing metallic minerals.

**Bladed habit:** flattened mineral resembling a knife blade.

**Blowpipe:** metal tube for producing a flame.

**Blue ground:** weathered second layer of kimberlite in diamond pipe.

**Body wave:** primary or secondary earthquake wave.

**Bolide:** bright meteor.

**Borate:** mineral containing boron.

**Border zone:** outer zone in pegmatite.

**Botryoidal habit:** globular mineral resembling a bunch of grapes.

**Brass:** alloy of copper and zinc.

**Brazil twin:** twin crystal of quartz.

**Breccia:** rock composed of angular or broken fragments.

**Brittleness:** tendency of a mineral to break into powder.

**Bromoform:** heavy liquid used to separate mineral grains or determine specific gravity.

**Bronze:** alloy of copper, tin, and zinc.

**Bronze Age:** middle period of prehistoric human culture.

**Building stone:** rock used for structural purposes.

**Butterfly twin:** twin crystal of quartz.

**Cabochon:** gem cut with rounded top.

**Caliche:** deposit of nitrate fertilizer in Chile.

**Cameo:** gem carved in relief.

**Capillary habit:** hair-shaped mineral.

**Carat:** unit of weight for a gem, 200 milligrams.

**Carbonaceous rock:** rock containing organic matter.

**Carbonate:** mineral composed of carbon, oxygen, and other elements.

**Cavestone:** stalactite or stalagmite.

**Cementation:** deposition of mineral matter between rock fragments.

**Chatoyancy:** shifting band of light on a mineral.

**Class:** one of 32 subdivisions into which crystals are classified according to symmetry.

**Clastic rock:** sedimentary rock consisting of fragments.

**Cleavage:** breakage of a mineral in definite directions along smooth surfaces, or of a rock into rough slabs.

**Closed tube:** hollow glass tube closed at one end, used in blowpiping.

**Coal Measures:** coal beds of Carboniferous age.

**Cohesion:** hardness or roughness of a mineral.

**Cold light:** ultraviolet radiation.

**Color:** particle of placer gold.

**Columnar habit:** pillar-shaped mineral.

**Compaction:** compression of sediment by pressure.

**Composite gem:** gem consisting of several parts put together.

**Compound:** union of chemical elements.

**Compressional wave:** primary earthquake wave.

**Concentration:** separation of valuable mineral or rock from waste.

**Conchiolin:** organic substance in shell of pearl mollusk.

**Conchoidal fracture:** shell-like breakage surface of a mineral or rock.

**Concretion:** nodule of foreign material in sedimentary rock.

**Consolidation:** change of sediment into solid rock.

**Contact metamorphism:** change at margin of igneous intrusion.

**Core:** innermost zone in pegmatite.

**Cosmic ray:** radiation shorter than gamma ray.

**Country rock:** unmineralized rock surrounding ore.

**Cross cut:** mine tunnel intersecting vein.

**Crust:** outer zone of the earth.

**Crystal:** solid body with regular atomic structure and flat external surfaces.

**Crystal chemistry:** science relating atomic structure and chemistry of crystals.

**Cube:** six-faced crystal form in isometric system.

**Cultured gem:** pearl grown by artificial methods.

**Cylinder:** long pierced bead.

**Dendritic habit:** flattened tree-shaped growth of manganese or iron oxide.

**Detrital rock:** sedimentary rock consisting of fragments.

**Diagnostic mineral:** mineral indicating the geologic environment.

**Dichroscope:** instrument for observing twin colors in a gem.

**Dike:** tabular body of igneous rock cutting across older rock.

**Dimension stone:** building stone cut to regular sizes.

**Dipotassium tartrate:** D.K.T., synthetic organic crystal used in telephone communication.

**Disturbance:** regional mountain-making event in earth history, separating two periods.

**Dodecahedron:** twelve-faced crystal form in isometric system.

**Doodlebug:** forked stick used to find ore or water.

**Double refraction:** separation of light into two rays.

**Doublet:** gem consisting of two parts put together.

**Dredge:** boat used to recover placer minerals.

**Drift:** mine tunnel parallel to vein.

**Dripstone:** stalactite or stalagmite in a cave.

**Drusy habit:** cluster of tiny crystals.

**Ductile:** capable of being drawn into wire.

**Dump:** pile of waste rock discarded in mining.

**Effervescence:** fizzing of carbonate mineral in acid.

**Elastic:** capable of springing back into position after being bent.

**Elbow twin:** twin crystal of rutile or zircon.

**Electromagnetic series:** radiation of all wave lengths, including visible light.

**Electron:** negative charge surrounding the nucleus of an atom.

**Electroscope:** instrument for detecting radioactivity.

**Element:** one of the fundamental kinds of chemical atoms composing all matter.

**Epoch:** division of geologic time, part of a period.

**Era:** largest division of geologic time.

**Ethylene diamine tartrate:** E.D.T., synthetic organic crystal used in telephone communication.

**Extrusive rock:** igneous rock formed upon the surface.

**Face:** outer surface on a crystal.

**Facet:** flat surface on a cut gem.

**Fairy cross:** twin crystal of staurolite.

**Fauna:** animal life.

**Ferro-alloy:** metal used to alloy with iron.

**Fertilizer mineral:** mineral used to supply soil nutriment.

**Fibrous fracture:** threadlike breakage surface of a mineral.

**Field classification:** classification of rocks by observing them in outcrop.

**Filiform habit:** matted shape of a mineral.

**Filler:** mineral used to add desired properties to manufactured products.

**Fineness:** parts per thousand of pure gold in native metal.

**Fireball:** bright meteor.

**Flora:** plant life.

**Flotation:** recovery of minerals by means of their adherence to chemical froth.

**Flour gold:** extremely fine particles of gold.

**Flow structure:** banding in igneous rock.

**Fluorescence:** emission of light during exposure to invisible radiation.

**Flux:** substance to reduce melting temperature.

**Foliated habit:** mineral that separates into leaves or scales.

**Foliation:** layered structure in metamorphic rock.

**Foraminifera:** one-celled animals which cause deposition of limestone.

**Form:** all similar faces on a crystal.

**Formula:** chemical composition expressed in symbols.

**Fossil:** remains or impression of ancient plant or animal.

**Fracture:** irregular breakage of mineral or rock.

**Fragmental texture:** broken grains in volcanic rock.

**Frequency:** number of wave lengths or vibrations per second.

**Fuel:** mineral resource used to produce energy.

**Fulgurite:** sand fused by lightning.

**Gamma ray:** radiation having length between X-ray and cosmic ray.

**Gangue:** waste rock in mineral deposit.

**Geiger counter:** instrument for detecting radioactivity.

**Geochemical prospecting:** searching for ore by chemical tests.

**Geode:** hollow concretion lined with crystals.

**Geologic time chart:** tabular record of divisions of earth history.

**Geologist's hammer:** rock hammer with pick or chisel edge.

**Geophysical prospecting:** searching for ore with scientific apparatus.

**Gilsonite:** asphaltic hydrocarbon found in veins in Utah and Colorado.

**Girdle:** equatorial plane of cut diamond.

**Glass wool:** mineral-wool insulation made from common glass.

**Glassy texture:** without mineral grains.

**Gloryhole:** mine combining open-cut and underground operations.

**Gossan:** iron oxide outcrop on sulfide vein.

**Grain:** mineral or glass constituent of rock.

**Granitic texture:** coarse-grained texture of intrusive igneous rocks.

**Granular habit:** aggregate of grains.

**Gravel:** loose rock coarser than sand.

**Gravimeter:** geophysical instrument for gravity prospecting.

**Greasy luster:** oily surface reflection of a mineral.

**Groundmass:** matrix of porphyry, surrounding phenocrysts.

**Group:** subdivision of chemical type of minerals.

**Grubstake:** supplies furnished to prospector in return for share in mineral discoveries.

**Habit:** shape or crystal form of a mineral.

**Hackly fracture:** jagged breakage surface of a metal.

**Half life:** time required for half of a radioactive element to disintegrate.

**Halide:** mineral composed of a halogen element and other elements.

**Hand specimen:** mineral or rock trimmed to about 3 x 4 x 1 inches.

**Hardness:** resistance of a mineral to being scratched.

**Hardness points:** set of minerals used to test hardness in Mohs' scale.

**Helictite:** twisted form of stalactite.

**Hexagonal:** one of the six crystal systems.

**Historical geology:** study of geologic history of the earth.

**Hydraulicking:** placer mining with jets of water.

**Hydroxide:** water-containing oxide mineral.

**Igneous rock:** rock cooled from molten magma or lava.

**Impurity:** minor amount of foreign element in a mineral.

**Inclusion:** mineral or rock surrounded by other material.

**Infrared ray:** heat ray longer than visible light.

**Inhibitor:** impurity preventing luminescence.

**Intaglio:** gem carved below surface.

**Intermediate zone:** zone between wall zone and core in pegmatite.

**Intrusive rock:** igneous rock formed below the surface.

**Ion:** electrically charged atom.

**Iron Age:** third period of prehistoric human culture.

**Iron cross:** twin crystal of pyrite.

**Iron hat:** iron oxide outcrop on sulfide vein.

**Isometric:** one of the six crystal systems.

**Isotopes:** elements having the same properties but slightly different weights.

**Japanese twin:** twin crystal of quartz.

**Jig:** equipment for recovering placer minerals.

**Jolly balance:** spring balance used to determine specific gravity.

**Karat:** parts per 24 of pure gold in alloy.

**Knee twin:** twin crystal of rutile or zircon.

**Lattice:** three-dimensional pattern of atoms in a crystal.

**Lava:** molten rock upon the surface.

**Level:** horizontal tunnel in mine.

**Lithification:** change of sediment into solid rock.

**Long wave:** surface earthquake wave.

**Longitudinal wave:** primary earthquake wave.

**Luster:** appearance of a mineral in reflected light.

**Magma:** molten rock below the surface.

**Magnetism:** ability to be attracted by a magnet.

**Magnetometer:** geophysical instrument for magnetic prospecting.

**Malleable:** capable of being pounded without breaking.

**Mammillary habit:** breast-shaped mineral.

**Massive habit:** lacking crystal form or imitative shape.

**Megascopic:** as observed in outcrop or hand specimen.

**Mercury vapor lamp:** source of short-wave ultraviolet light.

**Metallic mineral:** mineral having metallic luster or yielding a metal.

**Metamorphism:** extensive change of rock or mineral.

**Meteor:** light caused by passage of meteorite through earth's atmosphere.

**Meteorite:** rock from outer space.

**Miarolitic cavity:** opening in pegmatite, often containing large crystals.

**Micaceous habit:** characteristic of a mineral whereby it separates into very thin sheets.

**Micromount:** small mounted crystals observed under a microscope.

**Microscopic:** as observed in thin section or fragments under a microscope.

**Microwave:** radiation longer than infrared.

**Milling:** separation of valuable mineral or rock from waste.

**Mine:** excavation for extracting ore, minerals, or rocks.

**Mineral fuel:** coal, petroleum, or natural gas.

**Mineral wool:** insulation made from melted and sheared minerals and rocks.

**Mohs' scale:** scale of hardness used for minerals.

**Molecule:** smallest amount of a compound having all its chemical properties.

**Monoclinic:** one of the six crystal systems.

**Monument stone:** rock used in memorials.

**Mother lode:** principal vein system of a region.

**Mother-of-pearl:** iridescent inner shell layer of pearl mollusk.

**Mullite:** aluminum oxide and silica, used in ceramics.

**Neumann lines:** fine parallel lines in etched meteorite.

**Neutron:** neutral particle in the nucleus of an atom.

**Nitrate:** nitrogen-bearing mineral used as fertilizer.

**Nonmetallic mineral:** mineral not having a metallic luster or not used for its metal content.

**Nuclear energy:** energy from disintegration of nucleus of atom.

**Nucleus:** center of an atom, including the protons and neutrons.

**Nugget:** particle of native metal.

**Ocher:** iron and clay mixture, used for yellow or red pigments.

**Octahedron:** eight-faced crystal form in isometric system.

**Oölitic rock:** rock consisting of small rounded particles.

**Open cut:** mine in surface opening.

**Open tube:** hollow glass tube open at both ends, used in blow-piping.

**Ore:** rock or mineral deposit yielding a metal profitably.

**Orient:** sheen of pearl.

**Orthorhombic:** one of the six crystal systems.

**Overburden:** waste rock overlying mineral or rock deposit.

**Oxide:** mineral composed of oxygen and other elements.

**Oxidizing flame:** outer part of blowpipe flame.

**Paste:** artificial glass gem.

**Pearly luster:** surface reflection of cleavable mineral.

**Period:** division of geologic time, part of an era.

**Persistent mineral:** mineral formed under various geologic conditions.

**Petrographic microscope:** microscope producing polarized light.

**Phaneritic texture:** coarse-grained texture of intrusive igneous rocks.

**Phantom:** earlier growth enclosed within a crystal.

**Phenocryst:** larger mineral embedded in groundmass of porphyry.

**Phosphate:** mineral composed of phosphorus, oxygen, and other elements.

**Phosphates:** phosphorus-bearing minerals used as fertilizer.

**Phosphorescence:** emission of light after exposure to invisible radiation.

**Photoelectricity:** electricity produced in a crystal by light.

**Piezoelectricity:** electricity produced in a crystal by pressure.

**Pillar:** stalactite and stalagmite joined together.

**Pinch and swell:** expansion and contraction of vein.

**Pipe:** cylindrical body of kimberlite, source of diamond.

**Planetesimal hypothesis:** theory that the planets grew from solid particles.

**Playa lake:** intermittent lake in undrained desert basin.

**Pocket:** cavity in rock.

**Polyp:** marine colonial animal, source of coral.

**Porphyritic texture:** texture of igneous rock containing phenocrysts in a groundmass.

**Potash mineral:** potassium-bearing mineral used as fertilizer.

**Powder method:** X-ray identification of powdered crystal.

**Precious metal:** gold, silver, or platinum.

**Preliminary wave:** primary or secondary earthquake wave.

**Primary wave:** longitudinal or compressional earthquake wave.

**Prismatic habit:** pencil-shaped mineral.

**Property:** characteristic of a mineral or a rock.

**Prospector's hammer:** rock hammer with pick or chisel edge.

**Proton:** positive charge in the nucleus of an atom.

**Pseudomorph:** mineral having the shape of the substance it replaced.

**Pycnometer:** bottle used to determine specific gravity.

**Pyritohedron:** twelve-faced crystal form in isometric system.

**Pyroclastic rock:** rock broken by volcanic explosion.

**Pyroelectricity:** electricity produced in a crystal by temperature changes.

**Quarry:** open-cut mine for extracting rock.

**Radioactivity:** spontaneous disintegration of atomic nucleus, with release of energy.

**Radioautograph:** image produced on film by radioactive mineral.

**Radioscope:** instrument for detecting radioactivity.

**Raise:** upward working from mine tunnel.

**Rare earth:** any of fifteen chemical elements between lanthanum and lutecium.

**Rare-earth mineral:** mineral containing cerium, thorium, and other rare-earth metals.

**Recrystallization:** growth of small grains into larger ones.

**Reducing flame:** middle part of blowpipe flame.

**Reduction:** recovery of metal from ore.

**Refining:** purification of metal.

**Reniform habit:** kidney-shaped.

**Replacement:** substitution by mineral matter.

**Resinous luster:** surface reflection of mineral resembling resin.

**Reticulated habit:** network of crystals.

**Revolution:** major mountain-making event in earth history, separating two eras.

**Riker mount:** paper-bound, glass-covered box for displaying specimens.

**Ripple mark:** swirl in sand made by wind or water.

**Rochelle salt:** synthetic crystal used in phonographs.

**Rock flour:** finely powdered rock carried by a glacier.

**Rock wool:** mineral-wool insulation made from iron blast-furnace slag.

**Rocker:** equipment for recovering placer minerals.

**Rosette:** concentric group of crystals resembling a flower.

**Salt dome:** upthrust body of rock salt.

**Sand:** small mineral grains, usually quartz.

**Scarab:** Egyptian representation of beetle.

**Scintillation counter:** instrument for detecting radioactivity.

**Scintilliscope:** instrument for detecting radioactivity.

**Secondary wave:** transverse earthquake wave.

**Sectile:** capable of being cut with a knife.

**Sediment:** loose rock material.

**Sedimentary rock:** rock deposited as fragments or from solution.

**Seismic wave:** earthquake wave.

**Seismograph:** instrument for recording earthquake waves.

**Series:** minerals showing continuous variation in properties.

**Shaft:** vertical or inclined entry to mine.

**Shower:** simultaneous fall of several meteorites.

**Sienna:** iron, manganese, and clay mixture, used for yellow or brown pigments.

**Silicate:** mineral composed of silicon, oxygen, and other elements.

**Siliceous abrasive:** mineral or rock composed of silica, used for cutting and polishing.

**Silicic rock:** acidic rock, having high content of silica.

**Silky luster:** surface reflection of fibrous mineral.

**Sink-and-float:** recovery of mineral by use of heavy suspension.

**Slag:** glassy waste material in smelting process.

**Slaty cleavage:** breakage of slate into thin slabs.

**Sluice box:** equipment for recovering placer minerals.

**Smelting:** reducing ore to metal in a furnace.

**Soil:** broken and decomposed rock and decayed organic matter.

**Space-group:** one of 230 subdivisions into which crystals are classified according to symmetry.

**Species:** independent mineral or major member of a series.

**Specific gravity:** relative weight of a substance compared to water.

**Spintharoscope:** instrument for detecting radioactivity.

**Splintery fracture:** sharp breakage surface of a mineral.

**Stalactite:** cave mineral growth resembling an icicle.

**Star stone:** gem showing asterism.

**Steel:** alloy of iron and carbon.

**Steelmaking metal:** iron or its alloys.

**Stellated habit:** star-shaped radiating crystals.

**Stokes' law:** the law that wave length of radiation is lengthened during luminescence.

**Stone:** rock or mineral having certain commercial uses.

**Stone Age:** oldest period of human culture, before the use of metals.

**Stratification:** bedding in sedimentary rock.

**Streak:** color of powdered mineral.

**Streak plate:** unglazed porcelain used to test streak.

**Striations:** closely spaced fine parallel lines.

**Strip mining:** recovery of overburden and rock from flat deposit near surface.

**Submetallic luster:** feebly metallic surface reflection of a mineral.

**Sulfate:** mineral composed of sulfur, oxygen, and other elements.

**Sulfide:** mineral composed of sulfur and a metal or semimetal.

**Sulfosalt:** mineral composed of sulfur, a metal, and a semimetal.

**Surface wave:** long earthquake wave.

**Swallow-tail twin:** twin crystal of gypsum.

**Synthetic mineral:** substance having the composition and properties of a natural mineral but made artificially.

**System:** one of six subdivisions into which crystals are classified according to axes.

**Tabular habit:** book-shaped mineral.

**Tarnish:** surface alteration of metallic mineral.

**Tenacity:** resistance of a mineral to being broken.

**Tetragonal:** one of the six crystal systems.

**Texture:** size, shape, and pattern of grains in a rock.

**Thermoluminescence:** emission of light produced by heat.

**Thin section:** transparent slice of rock mounted on glass slide.

**Thumb mark:** pit in surface of meteorite.

**Thumbnail specimen:** mineral or crystal about one-half inch across.

**Till:** unsorted glacial deposit.

**Titania:** synthetic rutile, titanium dioxide.

**Torsion balance:** geophysical instrument for gravity prospecting.

**Toughness:** resistance to being broken.

**Transistor:** crystal used to record electrical impulses.

**Transverse wave:** secondary earthquake wave.

**Trapezohedron:** twenty-four-faced crystal form in isometric system.

**Treated gem:** gem artificially changed in color.

**Triboluminescence:** emission of light produced by friction.

**Triclinic:** one of the six crystal systems.

**Triplet:** gem consisting of three parts put together.

**Twin crystal:** two or more crystals intergrown in a definite way.

**Twin law:** law stating the way in which the parts of a twin crystal are related.

**Type:** subdivision of chemical class of minerals.

**Ultramarine:** blue mineral pigment, formerly made from lapis lazuli.

**Ultraviolet ray:** radiation shorter than visible light, causes luminescence.

**Umber:** iron, manganese, and clay mixture, used for brown pigments.

**Unit cell:** smallest amount of a crystal lattice having all its properties.

**Vanadate:** mineral composed of vanadium, oxygen, and other elements.

**Variety:** subdivision of a mineral species.

**Vein:** stringer of ore in rock.

**Visor twin:** twin crystal of cassiterite.

**Vitreous luster:** glassy surface reflection of a mineral.

**Volcanic bomb:** rounded lava erupted by volcano.

**Vulcanism:** effects of molten rock and volcanoes.

**Wall zone:** zone between border and intermediate zones in pegmatite.

**Wave length:** distance between similar points on successive waves.

**Widmanstätten figures:** intersecting bands in etched meteorite.

**Winze:** a passageway to permit downward working from mine tunnel.

**X-ray:** radiation having length between ultraviolet and gamma rays.

**Yellow ground:** oxidized upper layer of kimberlite in diamond pipe.

**Yellow sand:** sand containing heavy nonmetallic minerals.

# Index

# Index